ERCD12

M36068. Y.07

GCSE Technology

D1549326

ELE

2

195602

GCSE TECHNOLOGY

Steve Rich   **Anthony Edwards**

Pneumatics
Mechanisms
Structures with Materials
Digital Electronics and Computer Control
Teacher's Support Pack

ELECTRONICS

Steve Rich

Head of Design, Weatherhead High School

Anthony Edwards

Head of Design Technology
at a Wirral Sixth Form College, Merseyside

Stanley Thornes (Publishers) Ltd

First published in 1990 by:
Stanley Thornes (Publishers) Ltd
Old Station Drive
Leckhampton
CHELTENHAM GL53 0DN
England

British Library Cataloguing in Publication Data

Rich, Steve
Electronics.
1. Electronics
I. Title   II. Edwards, Anthony   III. Series
537.5

ISBN 0-7487-0153-2

Diagrammatic artwork by Mark Dunn
Typeset in 11/12½ Italia by Tech-Set, Gateshead, Tyne & Wear
Printed and bound in Great Britain at The Bath Press, Avon

Acknowledgements

The authors and publishers wish to acknowledge with thanks the following sources of photographs:

Adam Leisure Ltd p. 8; Belling & Co. Ltd p. 2 (H); Boss Industrial Mouldings p. 75 *bottom*; Intertan UK Ltd p. 5 *centre right*; The National Grid Company plc p. 5 *left*; Philips Consumer Electronics p. 2 (G): Philips Home Appliances p. 2 (B); Philips Major Appliances p. 2 (E); RS Components pp. 4 *centre*, 6, 19, 32 *top*, 33 *left*, 46 *right*, 69, 70, 71, *top*, 78, 88; A. Russell p. 50.

All other photographs were taken by Claire Starkey.

Contents

Preface

This book is designed to be a self-contained course that will be 'user friendly' to both student and teacher. It contains a series of graded design problems that can be used sequentially or independently. This allows flexibility in the use of the material.

The book takes into account the varied requirements of the National Curriculum through the medium of high technology. It has been tried and tested as a teaching and reference material for students preparing for GCSE technology examinations (equivalent to Key Stage 4).

The authors recognise that not all schools have the same level of equipment and therefore the development of a specification for each design brief has been omitted. It is envisaged that this can be developed by the students, who need to be aware of the equipment available to them.

Chapter 16 provides background information which students can refer to as and when necessary. It includes general introductions to components such as resistors, transistors and switches which are used in many circuits in the book, as well as sections on useful techniques such as soldering, circuit building using various systems and tracking down faults in a circuit once constructed.

All diagrams in this book have been drawn to British Standards. All circuits have been thoroughly tested.

Steve Rich   Anthony Edwards
1990

CHAPTER 1

Students' guide to the book

Every chapter contains information on a particular aspect of electronics together with a theoretical and practical activity to help you to develop your understanding. Each new section builds on the work done earlier in the book. Additional activities are contained in the teacher's book for this series.

When doing practical work you should be aware that incorrect use of electronic devices and power supplies can be dangerous. We recommend that you read Chapter 7 *Safety* before starting your practical work.

Note: All the circuits constructed during the activities in this book use a low voltage d.c. supply, (maximum voltage 12 V d.c.).

As you read through the book you will find that each section can be used on its own to explore a particular topic or idea or it can be combined with the others to give you a complete course in electronics.

To avoid confusing detail the *analysis/research* sections do not include all the work needed to fully design and install a complete solution to the design problems. You will need to add more information if you are to model the solutions accurately. The *Research* section (Chapter 16) in the back of this book will provide you with some of the additional information you will need.

You may not need to read all the chapters. Seek your teacher's advice on which sections of this book are most important in terms of your examination syllabus. If you do complete every chapter, your project work will be helped by having a wider understanding of electronic systems.

Good luck!

CHAPTER 2

Introduction to electricity

Everyone uses electricity

A simple activity like turning on a torch to light your way involves the use of electricity. Electricity is also used in a personal stereo to move the cassette tape past the playback head and to produce the sound of the recording in the earphones. Many families use electricity to provide heat for cooking and warming the home.

'The use of electricity is so common that you could be excused for taking it for granted'. Try to imagine a period of time when this statement could not be used. How long ago would it be?

 ASSIGNMENT 2.1

Look at the photographs below and match each modern item with its older relative. State what period of time the older version belongs to (e.g. 1920).

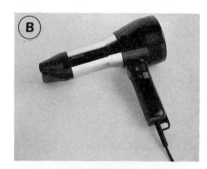

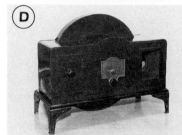

Select one item and compare the older version with the modern one. Complete a list of the differences between them.

Basic electronics

Current

Materials are made up of molecules which contain one or more **atoms**.

Atoms consist of a positively charged **nucleus** surrounded by negatively charged **electrons.** Electrons move around the nucleus in different orbits. Those close to the nucleus are bonded by a strong attraction to it. Those further away are free to move out of orbit.

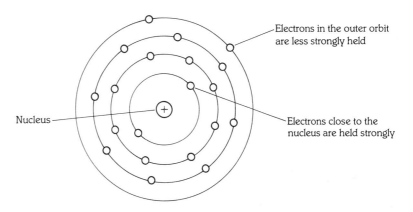

Nucleus

Electrons in the outer orbit are less strongly held

Electrons close to the nucleus are held strongly

If the free electrons are persuaded to move in one direction an electric current is produced. Electrical current is measured in amperes, or **amps** for short (symbol A). The symbol for current is I.

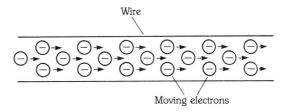

Wire

Moving electrons

Conductors

Free-flowing electrons require a path or circuit to flow through in order to do useful work. This is provided by materials which are called conductors.

Some of the best conductors are metals and impure water. Water is an impractical conductor in most situations. Two of the most conductive metals are gold and copper. Gold is a precious metal and too expensive to use in the large quantities needed for general electrical work. The cheaper alternative of copper is used.

Wires made from copper are used to connect electrical components in a **circuit.** This wire is covered with PVC which prevents 'short circuits' (electrons moving along a route that is not desirable). Wires that need to be stiff are made from a single copper strand. Breaks can occur in this kind of wire if it is stressed. Flexible cables are made from many thin strands of fine wire. They are used in situations where bending is frequent. Most household appliances are connected to a power supply by flexible, multi-strand wire.

Single copper wire (*top*) and multi-strand wire (*bottom*)

The flow of electricity through a conductor will generate heat. If the wire is too thin more heat will be generated than the wire can get rid of. It may overheat and burn through. It is therefore important to choose the correct size of wire. Wires that need to carry a large electrical current will be thicker than wires used for low currents.

Wires can be connected together in many ways to form a circuit. Mechanical clamps can be used to hold them together.

Two different types of mechanical connector

Wires can also be connected by careful soldering. A lead and tin mixture that melts at a lower temperature than the copper is used to join them together.

A good soldered joint

Insulators

Insulators, mainly non-metals and liquids (including pure water), do not allow a current to flow. Plastics and some ceramic materials are the best insulators.

Some uses of insulators: (*left*) on an electricity pylon, (*right, from top*) insulated wire, DIN plug and socket, electrician's insulated screwdriver

Insulators help to isolate conductors from each other, preventing unwanted electrical flow. They allow us to use electricity safely.

Semiconductors

Some materials (silicon and germanium) are conductors in some situations and insulators in others. They are known as semi-conductors and are extremely important in modern electronics.

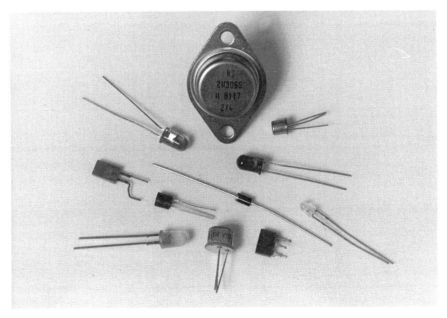

Some electronics components that depend on semiconductors

5

Voltage

The force required to produce a flow of free electrons is called the **electromotive force** (e.m.f.) and is measured in **volts.** Its symbol is V. This force is provided by a power source, such as a battery. As the electrons pass through a power source they are given energy. This can be converted by a **transducer** (e.g. a heating element in a fire) into another form of energy such as light, heat, sound or motion.

Water level sensor

Bimetallic temperature sensor

Rotational position sensor

Some transducers

The amount of electrical energy converted by a transducer is represented by the voltage difference across the component. This is sometimes referred to as the **potential difference** (p.d.) and is also measured in volts (V).

Potential difference can occur without a current flowing. A current cannot occur without a potential difference and a complete circuit. What do you think a 'complete circuit' means?

Power

The speed at which the energy transfer occurs is called **power.** The power consumption of any device is calculated by multiplying the potential difference across it (V volts) by the current (I amps) passing through it. Power is measured in **watts,** and its symbol is P.

$$P \text{ watts} = V \text{ volts} \times A \text{ amps}$$

Example
How much power does an electric motor use if the voltage across it is 5 volts and the current through it is 0.2 amps? Using the formula above,

$$
\begin{aligned}
P \text{ watts} &= V \text{ volts} \times A \text{ amps} \\
&= 5\,\text{V} \times 0.2\,\text{A} \\
P &= 1 \text{ watt}
\end{aligned}
$$

This is a very important calculation because the cost of our domestic electricity is based on **power consumption**. This is measured in kilowatt hours: 1 kilowatt hour = 1000 watts for one hour.

Supplying electricity

You may be familiar with two types of battery, those in motor cycles and cars and those used to power a radio or a cassette player. Both types use a chemical reaction between two different metals and an electrolyte to produce an electromotive force. In a car battery the electrolyte is a liquid (wet) and in a cassette player battery the electrolyte is in the form of a dry paste (well, very nearly!). This is where the terms **wet cell** and **dry cell** originate.

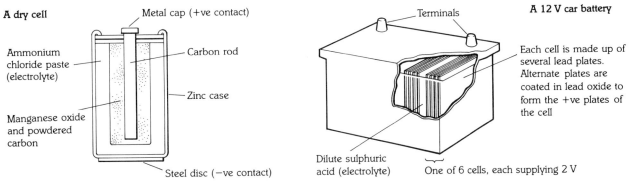

A dry cell

Metal cap (+ve contact)

Ammonium chloride paste (electrolyte)

Carbon rod

Zinc case

Manganese oxide and powdered carbon

Steel disc (−ve contact)

A 12 V car battery

Terminals

Each cell is made up of several lead plates. Alternate plates are coated in lead oxide to form the +ve plates of the cell

Dilute sulphuric acid (electrolyte)

One of 6 cells, each supplying 2 V

Both these types of cells produce a **direct current** (d.c.) that remains at a constant voltage and flows through a circuit in one direction only.

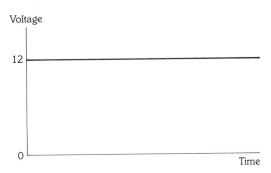

Voltage

12

0

Time

This is a graphical representation of d.c. voltage. Dry batteries have one major disadvantage. They can only provide electrical energy while the chemical reaction occurs between the electrolyte and the metals. When this reaction is exhausted the cell will not produce any further energy.

Rechargeable batteries (Ni-Cads), in which this chemical reaction can be reversed, have been developed in the past few years. They are relatively expensive when compared with normal batteries but they can be recharged and used many times over before they expire.

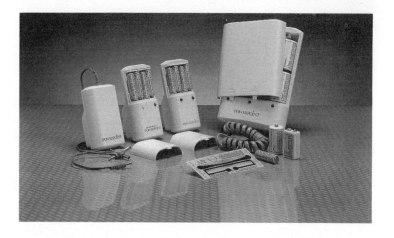

Some types of battery can be recharged in special battery rechargers

The d.c. electricity from batteries or stabilised power supply units (PSU) is represented by these symbols:

Single cell   Multiple cell

Another source of electrical energy can be obtained from the domestic mains. This supplies electricity in the form of **alternating current** (a.c.). In alternating current the voltage constantly changes from a maximum positive voltage to a maximum negative voltage.

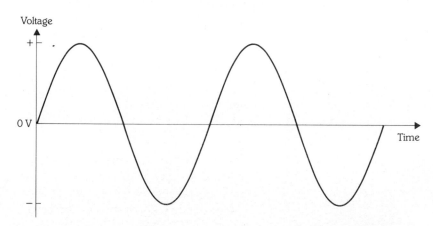

This picture represents what happens to the voltage. The current flows first in one direction through the circuit and then in the opposite direction. This happens 50 times a second in the mains supply.

The domestic mains is usually referred to as being a 250 V supply. If it is measured, the actual voltage from zero to peak is about 335 V. The *average* value of an alternating voltage is called its **r.m.s.** value. This is about 240 V for the mains supply. The abbreviation r.m.s. is short for the root mean square. In simple terms it means the 'average' voltage for a.c. Ask your maths teacher for an accurate explanation. Be warned, take a chair and a notebook, the answer may not be short!!

High voltage alternating current is the best way to send electricity along long cables. This method can pass a large quantity of electrical energy with the lowest losses. The voltage of the main supply lines that transfer electricity around the country is very high, about 400 000 volts! This high voltage is 'stepped down' to 240 V for normal domestic consumption.

ASSIGNMENT 4.1

When nuclear reactors were first introduced, it was expected that the cost of electricity would fall. This has not proved to be the case and the price has continued to rise. What factors do you think would affect the cost of producing electricity by conventional and non-conventional means?

Do not forget to consider the costs to the environment.

ACTIVITY 4.1

Write a short article to appear in a local newspaper that gives a balanced view of how the production of electricity and its consequences affect the area where you live.

CHAPTER 5

Electronic systems

A solar system, such as the one that the Earth belongs to, is a group of planets that move in fixed orbits around one central body, i.e. a sun. Although each planet has its own geography and climate it is affected by other bodies in the group. It is therefore important to consider them as a collective whole — a **system**.

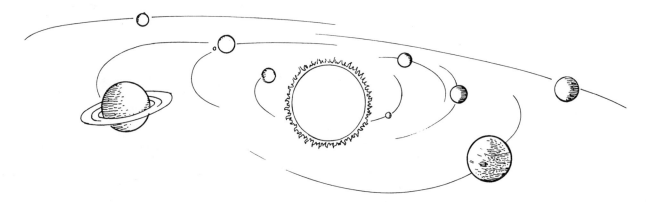

Scientists, designers and engineers often look at the behaviour of a collection of individual items and consider them to be one unit. The study of systems leads to more creative thinking for all these people.

Individual electronic components (**discrete** devices) have their own characteristics which vary greatly. It would be difficult to learn to design in electronics if you first had to understand fully how all these discrete devices worked. It is more important to understand what you want them to do when they are combined and act as a system.

The designer of electronic devices uses '**systems**' thinking to help to solve the problems he or she has been set.

Example of a system

Your body acts as a system which responds to all sorts of changes:

If the air around you becomes cold, your skin (acting as a heat sensor) detects the drop in temperature. This information is sent to the brain through the nervous system.

The brain responds and instructs the body to generate warmth.

This is done by converting stored energy into heat by flexing the muscles (shivering).

In this example there are three features that can be found in any system.

Input
The input of any system is a change in condition or state that will influence the output. In the example we are considering, the skin senses the drop in temperature.

Control or process
This is the stage in any system that allows the transfer or conversion of information provided by the input. In the example we are considering, the brain receives the signals from the skin and **processes** this information. Other parts of the body are then alerted and ordered to take action.

Output
This can take many forms. It is a predictable end result (output) from a known set of input conditions. In the example we are considering, shivering will occur whenever the brain senses that the body is too cold. This is a reflex action. There are also conscious actions that can be taken to generate heat, such as exercise or putting on additional clothes.

This is how we would represent this system as a flow diagram:

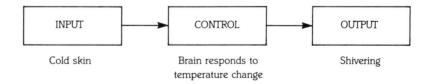

INPUT		CONTROL		OUTPUT
Cold skin		Brain responds to temperature change		Shivering

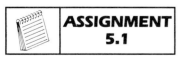

ASSIGNMENT 5.1

Select a machine or device in your home and analyse it in systems terms. Draw a diagram (like the one above) to explain your thinking.

A simple circuit

Design problem

A younger member of your family would like to make a new electrical toy. There are plenty of raw materials available and you have been asked to help. Remember that in order to create this toy you will need a power source and a complete circuit. Do not attempt to use a soldering iron. Make all joints with mechanical connectors.

Design brief

Using items such as those listed below, design and make a simple, electrically powered toy that will amuse a young member of your family.

Analysis/research

Children like toys that move.
Lights attract young children's attention.
Toys must be safe.
Children don't like boring toys.
The age of a child will affect the type of toy he or she likes.
The device must not be powered from the mains.

Suitable materials

Batteries and battery holder	Silver foil
Paper clips	Low voltage bulb and holder
Wooden strips	Paper fasteners
Motors	Wooden discs
Wire	Drawing pins
Connectors	Elastic bands
LEDs with resistors	

Useful Tools

Adhesive tape	PVC insulating tape
Glue gun and glue	Paper/card glues
Scissors	Modelling knife
Hand drill and drills	Junior hacksaw
Long-nosed pliers	Wire cutters
Small screwdriver	

Design solution

A possible solution to the design problem is as follows.

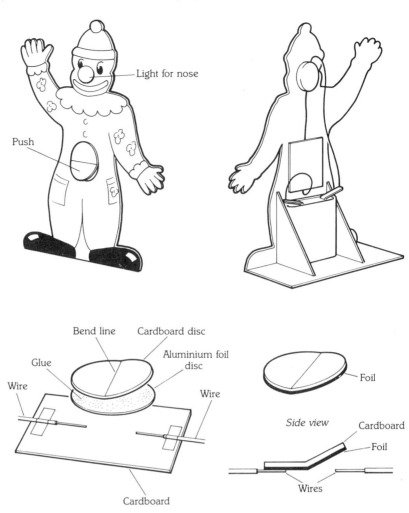

Light for nose

Push

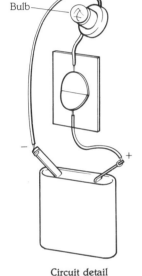

Bulb

Circuit detail

Bend line — Cardboard disc

Aluminium foil disc

Glue

Wire

Wire

Foil

Side view

Cardboard

Foil

Cardboard

Wires

Switch detail

This is not a final solution. The components need to be attached to the cardboard base so that the foil will complete the circuit only when the disc is pressed. How would you do this?

Description of circuit
The switch operates when the foil contact plate bridges the gap between the connecting wires. This causes the light to be switched on.

The drawings above took a long time to produce and could easily misrepresent the ideas they were designed to explain. In electronics, symbols are used to avoid these difficulties.

In circuit diagrams wires are shown as solid lines:

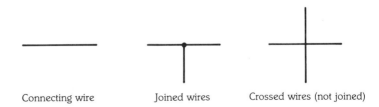

Connecting wire   Joined wires   Crossed wires (not joined)

Be very careful not to confuse crossed wires with joined wires. If there is a dot where the wires cross then they are joined. *Separate* and *insulated* wires will not have a dot where they meet or cross.

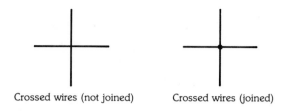

Crossed wires (not joined)   Crossed wires (joined)

It is good practice to avoid confusion by rearranging the drawing so that connecting lines do this:

Non-connecting crossed wires will not be confused so easily if this is done. The switch operates when the foil contact plate bridges the gap between the connecting wires. This causes the light to be switched on. The symbols for a switch and a lamp are:

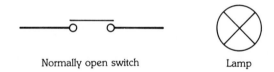

Normally open switch   Lamp

The symbol for a power source was given in Chapter 4.

By combining the symbols above the **circuit diagram** for the toy can be drawn as follows:

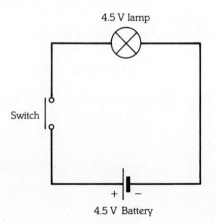

4.5 V lamp

Switch

4.5 V Battery

When symbols are used for the electronic components the completed diagram is accurate and clear. The symbols enable you to communicate your ideas quickly.

Evaluation

When you have designed, constructed and tested your device, explain its good and bad points. What things would you improve if you made it again?

One of the weaknesses in the design of the circuit above was the switch. It could be easily damaged. A more robust design would be better. Switches should be reliable, tough and safe.

In Chapter 16 (pages 80–83) a wide range of different switches is shown. Read the section and make notes on five different types of switches that you think will be useful in your design work. Use catalogues from different suppliers and compare:

1) the price of each switch,
2) the maximum voltage or working voltage and maximum current that can be tolerated by each switch.

ASSIGNMENT 6.1

1) Look up the circuit symbols for the following devices: light source (lamp), LED, buzzer, bell, motor and battery. Record these for your future use.

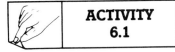

ACTIVITY 6.1

Assemble and test the circuit shown on page 14 using either an electronics kit or individual components. Do you think that it is safe to be used by very young children?

Safety

High voltage and current can maim and kill! Even low voltage devices like batteries and power packs can deliver a painful shock. The human body has a natural resistance to the flow of electricity but when this resistance is reduced or overcome then the body will receive an electric shock.

Electricity can be dangerous. It is very important that you follow a number of sensible rules when working with electricity.

1) **Never undertake any activity in electronics unless you have the approval of a competent adult and understand what you are doing.**

2) **Do not experiment with mains electricity.**

3) **Mains equipment, including low voltage supply units, should be connected to a circuit breaker.**

4) **Only use equipment that meets approved safety standards.**

5) **Never mix water and mains electricity.**

6) **Do not touch electrical devices with wet hands.**

7) **Turn off any electrical device and unplug it before attempting to work on it.**

ASSIGNMENT 7.1

1) Discuss with your teacher the topic of electrical safety.

2) Produce a list of simple common-sense safety rules, to add to those above, that should be followed when working with electricity. List them in order of importance.

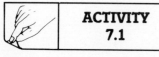

ACTIVITY 7.1

Draw a design for a poster that will help to educate people and help them to live safely with electricity.

Resistors

Design problem

Because your younger brother or sister has developed a fear of the dark he/she insists on going to bed with a light on. This is a situation that your parents wish to discourage.

Design brief

You have been asked to design a cheap and robust night light to reassure your brother or sister when going to bed. It should help with the child's adjustment to sleeping in the dark.

Analysis/research

The solution should be battery powered because:

a) The use of mains electricity is to be strongly discouraged in a project of this kind. The dangers to you and the young child using the device are numerous — can you list them?

b) The room is always untidy, leaving little space for a conventional lamp and its cable.

The device should appeal to a young child. Its shape should reflect the interests of your brother or sister.

Any switches or controls should be simple to operate.

The cost of construction should be kept low.

The design solution should be safe.

It should be strong and robust.

Battery life should be conserved.

In systems terms the following should be true:

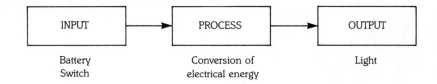

To make the battery last longer we need a component that will restrict the movement of free electrons in the circuit. All components do this but some are more limiting than others. Components which are designed to restrict electron flow in a predetermined way are called **resistors.** Resistance (symbol *R*) is measured in **ohms.** The symbol for this is the Greek capital letter omega, Ω.

The simplest form of resistor is a metal wire. The longer the wire, the greater the resistance. A special **resistance wire** is commercially available for this purpose.

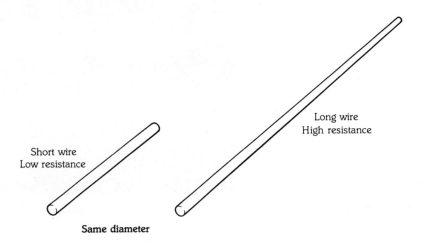

The resistance of the wire can also be increased by reducing its thickness (cross-sectional area).

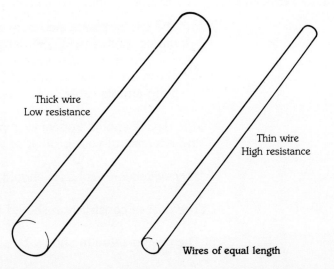

If both these wires are exactly the same length, then the one with the smaller cross-sectional area will have the higher resistance to the passage of electricity.

Design solution 1

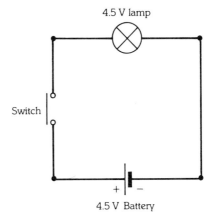

4.5 V lamp

Switch

+ −

4.5 V Battery

If a small reistance is added to this circuit (used in Chapter 6) by including a length of resistance wire it will cause two changes.

1) The bulb will be dimmed.
2) The flow of electrons will be reduced, helping to conserve battery life.

The new circuit will look like this:

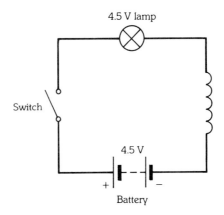

4.5 V lamp

Switch

4.5 V

+ −

Battery

Resistance wire is not normally used for this type of work because long lengths are required to achieve large resistances. Smaller components are used. These are called **fixed resistors.** They are commonly made from carbon or metal oxide.

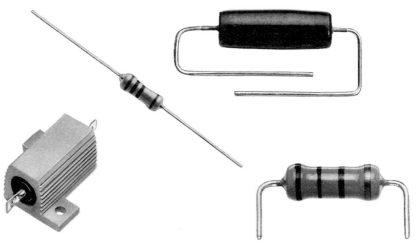

Fixed resistors come in different shapes and sizes

Design solution 2

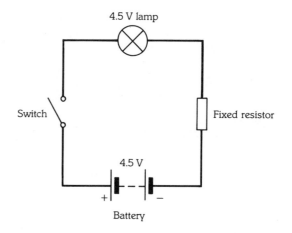

4.5 V lamp

Switch

Fixed resistor

4.5 V

Battery

In this circuit all the components are connected in **series** (linked together in a chain).

The components will need to be joined together by soldering. They should be mounted on a board so that they will be kept in place. Use the section on soldering in Chapter 16 to find out how this is done.

Evaluation

The resistor value is very important. If it is too high the lamp will not be bright enough! If it is too low the light will be bright, but the battery life will be shorter.

A better solution would allow the level of light to be varied to suit the conditions. By gradually reducing the light level your brother or sister will become used to sleeping in the dark.

To vary the light level we must be able to change the resistance in the circuit easily.

Research/analysis

In the original discussion of this design problem a resistance wire was used to illustrate how the flow of electrons in a circuit could be restricted. By altering the working length of the resistance wire we can obtain a range of potential differences across the bulb.

In the diagram below this is done by moving the sliding contact along the wire. To dim the light the slider should be moved to the left. Can you explain why?

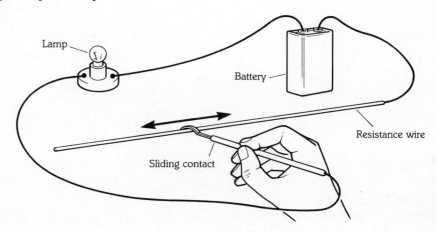

Lamp

Battery

Resistance wire

Sliding contact

A commercially available component that will replace the long length of resistance wire is called a **variable resistor.**

Design solution 3

In this solution the fixed resistor has been replaced by a variable resistor (in practice a value of 470 Ω is suitable).

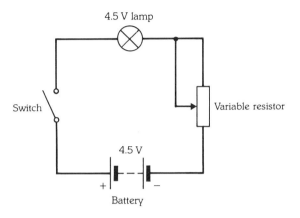

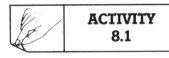

ACTIVITY 8.1

Using the components available to you, build the circuit shown above. Test it and check that it works. If there are problems check each of the connections in the circuit, including the joint that makes up the bulb holder! If you have further problems, refer to the fault finding section in Chapter 16 (page 70).

ASSIGNMENT 8.1

Answer the following questions on the circuit that you have built.

1) Did the circuit work the first time that you tested it? If it didn't work what did you find that was wrong?

2) Does the circuit look neat and tidy? How could it be packaged to make it look marketable?

3) Could the circuit be made smaller? How?

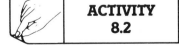

ACTIVITY 8.2

Compile a data table for your own use. Include information on:

1) resistor colour code

2) resistor types

3) resistor tolerances

4) 'preferred values' series

5) relative costs.

Potential divider circuits

Design problem	Your school has just been given a number of 9 volt power packs and a quantity of discrete components that are rated at 4.5 volts and 6 volts. When using these components it is important not to exceed the maximum voltage rating.

Design brief

You have been asked to investigate the problem described above and to design and make a simple circuit board that can provide two different voltages, 4.5 and 6 volts, from a 9 volt supply.

Analysis/research

The circuit will need to be simple and cheap to construct.

It must be easy to operate.

It must be robust (think of the number of different pupils who are likely to use it!).

In systems terms the following must be true:

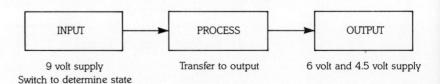

INPUT		PROCESS		OUTPUT
9 volt supply Switch to determine state		Transfer to output		6 volt and 4.5 volt supply

If we use two resistors in series connected across the positive and negative rails of a power supply (as in the diagram) we know from the previous chapter that there will be a voltage difference across each resistor.

If R_1 and R_2 are equal then the supply voltage will be spread evenly across both the resistors. This means that the voltage at point B will be half the supply voltage.

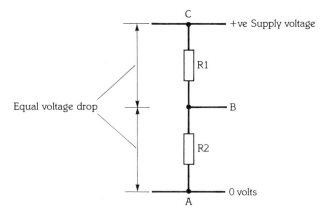

If the resistance R_1 is smaller than resistance R_2 then the voltage drop between C and B is *smaller* than that between B and A. The voltage at point B would be over half of the supply voltage.

The diagram below should help you to understand this.

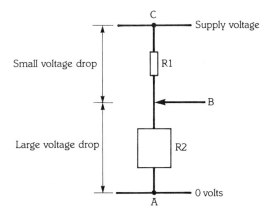

If R_1 is larger than R_2 then the voltage drop between C and B would be greater than that between B and A. The voltage at point B will be less than half of the supply voltage. See the diagram below.

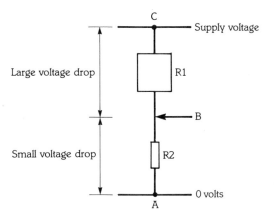

In electronics we need to be more precise than *large* or *small*. The following formula is used to work out what the exact voltage at point B will be.

Equation

$$\text{Voltage at point B } (V_{out}) = \text{Voltage at point C } (V_{in}) \times \frac{R_2}{(R_1 + R_2)}$$

Let $R_1 = 100\ \Omega$, $R_2 = 100\ \Omega$ and $V_{in} = 9\ V$

then
$$V_{out} = 9 \times \frac{100}{100 + 100} = \frac{100}{200} \times 9$$

$$V_{out} = \frac{1}{2} \times 9$$

$$V_{out} = 4.5 \text{ volts}$$

In the research section (Chapter 16) there is a model calculation showing how you can calculate the value of R_2 required to give you the value of V_{out} you want. In this case, for $V_{out} = 6$ volts you need $R_2 = 200\ \Omega$. The nearest resistor value available is $220\ \Omega$.

In order to obtain two outputs of 4.5 and 6 volts we will require the following arrangement of resistors:

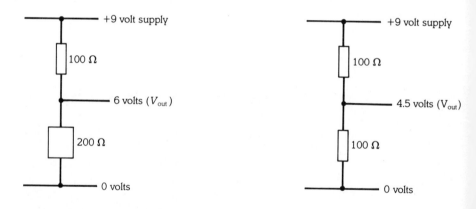

Design solution 1

Combining the two circuits drawn above with a single-pole double-throw switch we get:

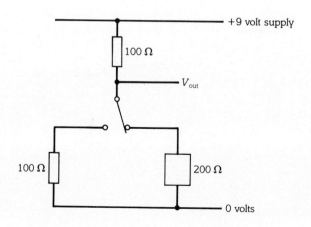

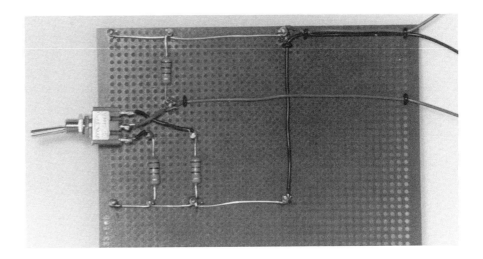

Design solution 1, on matrix board

ASSIGNMENT 9.1

Evaluation

1) What will the output voltage be from this circuit in the state shown?

2) What other voltage is available?

3) Will this design fulfill the design brief?

4) Find out how much it will cost to make this circuit.

5) Did you consider resources such as time, energy and equipment when you estimated the cost?

Design solution 2

An alternative circuit design could use the properties of resistors in parallel.

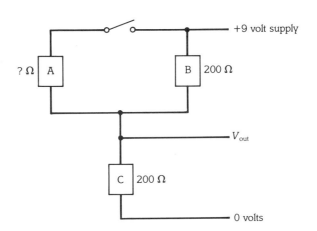

If the switch is open, resistor A is disconnected from the circuit. Resistors B and C in series will produce a V_{out} of 4.5 volts.

When the switch is closed resistors A and B are in parallel. In this state the circuit needs to produce a V_{out} of 6 volts. This can be achieved by making the total resistance of A and B combined equal to 100 Ω.

We use the following equation to work out the value of resistor A.

$$\frac{1}{R_{total}} = \frac{1}{R_A} + \frac{1}{R_B}$$

Given that R_{total} equals 100 Ω

and R_B equals 200 Ω

then, putting in the known values:

$$\frac{1}{100} = \frac{1}{R_A} + \frac{1}{200}$$

Transferring across:

$$\frac{1}{100} - \frac{1}{200} = \frac{1}{R_A}$$

Converting to equivalent fractions:

$$\frac{2}{200} - \frac{1}{200} = \frac{1}{R_A}$$

Subtracting:

$$\frac{1}{200} = \frac{1}{R_A}$$

Inverting the equation gives us the answer:

$$200 \text{ Ω} = R_A$$

The diagram shows the completed design with calculated values.

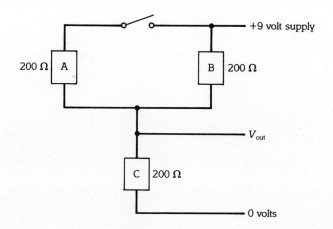

Design solution 2, on matrix board

ASSIGNMENT 9.2

Evaluation

Use the questions in Assignment 9.1 to evaluate Design solution 2.

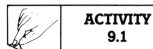
ACTIVITY 9.1

Using your evaluation as a guide, choose the best circuit and

1) Make a list of all the components that you need.

2) Use the research section (Chapter 16) to help you to design and make the smallest layout for the completed circuit.

3) Design and make a package that will completely house the finished circuit. Don't forget that the sockets and switches also take up some space inside the case.

4) Calculate an accurate cost for your solution.

5) Evaluate your design against the original specification. If there are any other designs available, compare them.

The transistor as a switch

Design problem

Breakfast was unusually tense this morning. You woke up, dressed quickly and went downstairs to find your mother fuming. The refrigerator door had not been closed properly when you took out your late night snack. An early departure for school looks like a good idea!

Design brief

You have been given two alternatives: either

a) do not go in the fridge at all! or,
b) make sure that the door is always closed. If you are careless you will have to pay for any damaged contents.

The first alternative is unbearable, therefore you need a device that will warn you if the door is not closed properly.

Research

Your solution must be cheap and durable.

It must have either a visual or audible alarm (or both).

It must not interfere with the efficient working of the fridge.

It must be powered by a low voltage supply.

Can you explain why the statements above have been made and can you add to them?

In systems terms the following should be true:

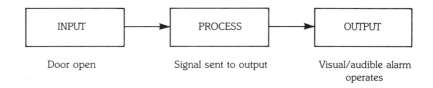

Door open   Signal sent to output   Visual/audible alarm operates

Design solution 1

The physical act of opening the door will provide a suitable signal for the device to operate. However, if you think about the system description:

Door open ➡ Alarm sounds

there appears to be a problem with using a normal S.P.S.T. (single-pole, single-throw) switch. This type of switch would cause the circuit to be complete and the alarm to sound when the door was closed.

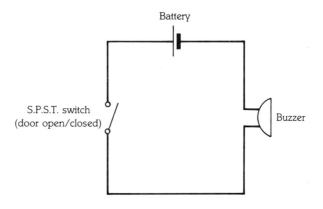

You could reverse (**invert**) the normal action of the circuit shown above.

Switch open ➡ Alarm on
Switch closed ➡ Alarm off

Another way of expressing this is to say that

INPUT   OUTPUT
Low signal ➡ High signal
High signal ➡ Low signal

A discrete component that will provide an inverted (high output from a low input) signal is a **transistor**.

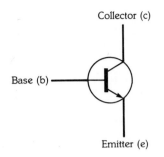

Base (b) ——

Symbol for an npn transistor

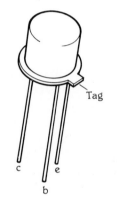

A BC108 transistor

Transistors normally have three connections called the base (b), the collector (c) and the emitter (e). It is very important that a transistor is connected the correct way around. To do this you must be able to identify the wires.

The transistor can be used as an electronic switch that has no moving parts. It is reliable, cheap and can switch many times per second without wearing out.

If a voltage of about 0.6 to 0.7 volts is applied to the base of the transistor the connection between the collector and emitter is complete. In this condition it is said to be **saturated** — *fully on.*

If the voltage is less than 0.6 to 0.7 volts then the connection between the collector and the emitter is incomplete — the transistor is fully off.

This is part of a typical transistor circuit:

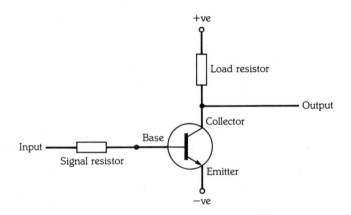

When a low voltage (less than 0.6 volts) is applied to the base of a transistor it will have a high internal resistance.
Note: the signal resistor protects the transistor from overload.

If the high internal resistance of the transistor (in the off state) is combined with an external (load) resistor in series, the output from the circuit will be high. (See Chapter 9).

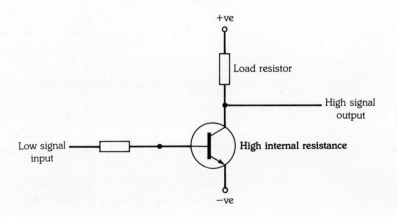

When the voltage applied to the base of the transistor is high (above the switching voltage of 0.6–0.7 volts) then the output will be low.

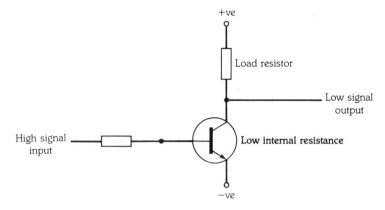

By combining the circuit above with a potential divider containing a set of contacts we get the following circuit:

COMPONENTS

R1	7 kΩ
R2	2 kΩ
R3	1 kΩ
R4	680 Ω
R5	330 Ω

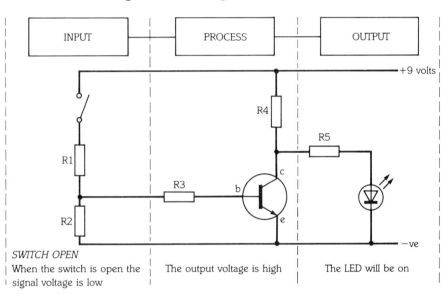

SWITCH OPEN
When the switch is open the signal voltage is low

The output voltage is high

The LED will be on

Design solution 1 on matrix board

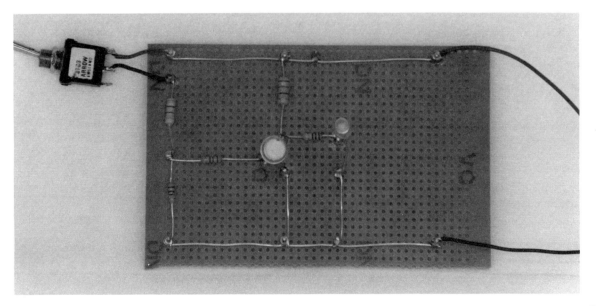

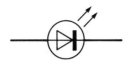

LED symbol

The output device used on the previous circuit is a **light emitting diode** (LED). This is a component that emits light when current flows through it in one direction.

It is very important to identify which side of the LED should be connected to the positive and negative rails of a circuit. This is done by looking at the body of the light. The flattened part of the body is nearest to the cathode (negative) leg.

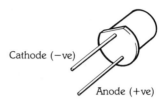

Cathode (−ve)

Anode (+ve)

LEDs can only tolerate a limited amount of current otherwise they are damaged. A protecting resistor is connected in series with the LED to limit the current flowing through it. See the circuit diagram below.

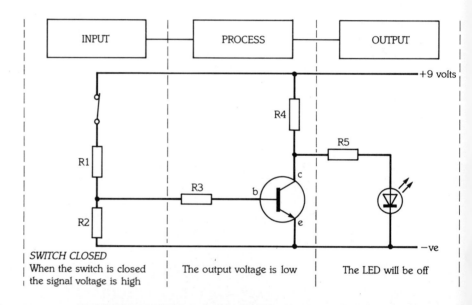

| INPUT | PROCESS | OUTPUT |

+9 volts

R4

R5

R1

R3   b   c

R2   e

−ve

SWITCH CLOSED
When the switch is closed the signal voltage is high | The output voltage is low | The LED will be off

Design solution 1 on Veroboard

Door contacts?

You can design and make a simple switch for the fridge by making two metal plates that are attached to the door and the fridge.

Alternatively, there are several different commercial designs of switch that could be used.

a) **Microswitch** — operated by a plate or bar that changes the switch's state.

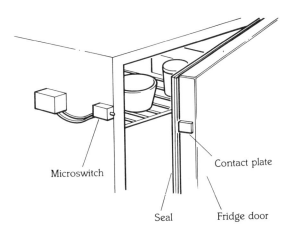

Microswitch

Contact plate

Seal

Fridge door

b) **Reed switch** — operated by either an external magnet or by using the magnetic strip that is built into the door.

See the research section (Chapter 16) for further information on switches.

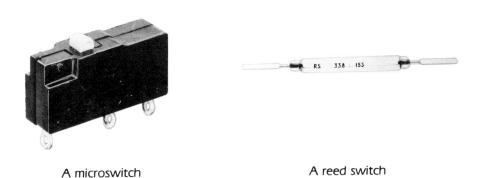

A microswitch

A reed switch

Evaluation

In general, the circuit fulfilled the design brief. There were problems with the wires from the switch unit. If the switch was positioned as far as possible from the hinged side of the door, there were visible trailing wires which interfered with the opening and closing of the door.

Keeping the contacts of the switch together when the door was closed can also be difficult. Some method of adjusting the position of the plate is required.

Fixing the switch unit to the fridge may present further difficulties.

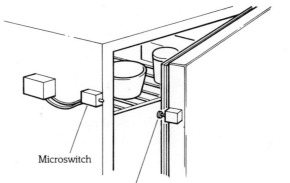

Microswitch

Switch contact screw – adjust to ensure good contact

Design solution 2

In Design solution 1 a set of simple contacts was used to sense the position of the fridge door. A more complicated system could be employed to sense other changes that occur when the fridge door is open.

What changes do you think occur when this happens?

The two obvious ones are

1) the temperature in the fridge rises, and
2) the internal light comes on.

Detecting a significant temperature change would be a method of sensing when the door had been left open. However, it would be slow and there would be many difficulties to overcome. Research a device that could be used to sense heat (see Chapter 11).

Detecting the state of the internal light is not as difficult. A discrete component that responds to different light levels by changing its resistance is called a **light dependent resistor** (LDR). This transducer has a high resistance when it is in the dark and a low resistance when light falls upon it.

COMPONENTS

VR1	100 kΩ
R1	1 kΩ
R2	680 Ω
R3	330 Ω
LDR	ORP 12
TR1	BC108
LED	

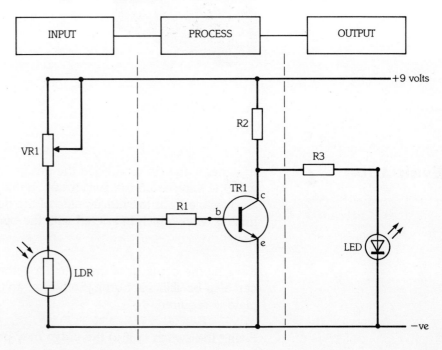

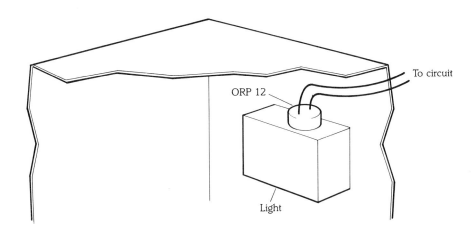

To circuit

ORP 12

Light

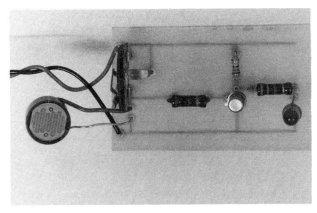

Design solution 2 on PCB

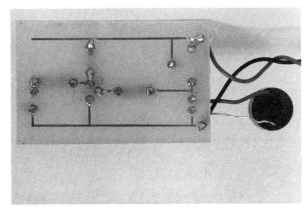

Underside of the PCB

Evaluation

The circuit worked well and fulfilled the design brief. There were problems with the wires from the LDR. These had to pass from the inside of the fridge to the outside. This included going through the seal on the door. There is a danger that the seal would be distorted and allow warm air to seep in.

ACTIVITY 10.1

Select one of the designs and make a fully working version suitable for production.

ASSIGNMENT 10.1

1) If you were to write a report on these solutions for a company which is interested in putting one of these designs into full scale production, what criteria would you use to evaluate them?

2) Using your criteria write an accurate and concise evaluation of both these circuits. (You may need to exchange information on the construction and design of these circuits with others in your group.)

Transistor amplifiers

| **Design problem** | A small market gardening company has to grow many of its plants from seeds or cuttings. These are cultivated inside a greenhouse which is next to the manager's house. If the temperature falls below a certain level then the growth of the cuttings or seeds is harmed. This would result in financial ruin for the grower.

As a new employee of the company its success or failure is very important to you. You have offered to investigate this problem.

Design brief

Your brief is to provide a solution which does not rely on constantly monitoring a thermometer inside the growing house.

Research/analysis

It is important to research and establish what the critical temperatures should be for healthy plant growth.

This is a newly formed company and expense is a very important factor. Any device needs to be very cost effective (and not cost a lot!).

You should be able to check that the system is operational at any time. It should be very reliable, failure could mean no job!

The sensor should be in the greenhouse (which is sometimes empty) but the warning system needs to be placed in the house.

The system should be easy to operate because any member of the household or company may need to respond to it.

The warning has to be easily recognisable.

The device should be easy to maintain.

In systems terms the following should be true:

INPUT	PROCESS	OUTPUT
Temperature falls below critical level	Singal sent to output	Visual/audible alarm operates

Thermistor symbol

A transducer that responds to temperature change is called a **thermistor**. This is a shortened version of thermo-sensitive resistor. Two main types are manufactured. The most common type has a negative temperature coefficient (NTC) which means that its resistance falls as the temperature rises.

The second type of thermistor, PTC, has a positive temperature co-efficient which means that its resistance increases as the temperature rises. These are usually used to protect certain types of circuit from overheating.

Thermistor

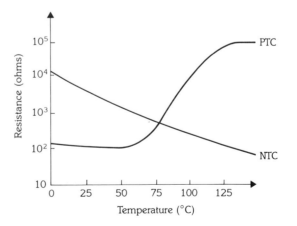

If a thermistor is connected in series with a resistor it will form a potential divider. This can provide a variable signal voltage which can be used to switch a transistor on and off.

Design solution 1

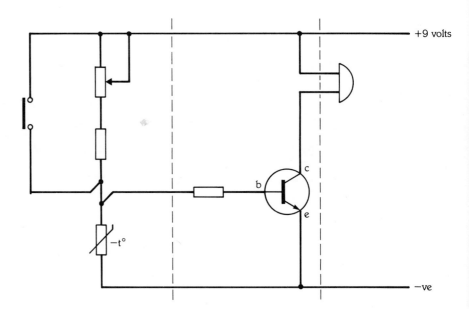

Test button

If the test button (a normally open push button switch) is pressed, the resistor is shorted out. This means that the signal voltage will be large enough to change the state of the transistor and cause the bell to ring.

Evaluation

There are two main problems with this circuit.

1) The buzzer/bell is very quiet. This is because the current driving the device is limited by the switching transistor.

2) The circuit is not very sensitive. If the temperature drops and rises again quickly the bell only sounds for the period in which the temperature is low. The office should be occupied at all times but in practice this is not the case. The warning could go unheeded!

Design solution 2

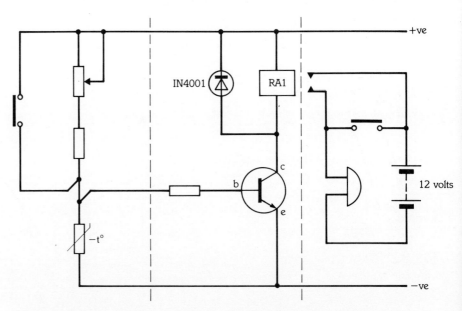

The switching circuit is still the same but the output is now connected to a new discrete component called a **relay**. A relay is an electro-mechanical switch that uses the magnetism generated by current passing through a coil to move a mechanical arm. This action forces a set of contacts together, which completes a circuit.

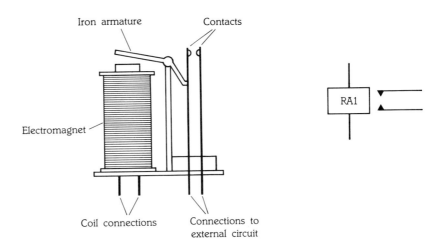

Iron armature   Contacts

Electromagnet

RA1

Coil connections   Connections to external circuit

The relay has many uses but in this situation it allows a second power supply to operate the bell without putting the transistor circuit at risk.

It is important to understand why a diode is always used in conjunction with a relay. When the power is turned off the relay is de-energised and a voltage is generated (called a back e.m.f.) which could damage the transistor. The diode is placed across the coil terminals to prevent this. Refer to the research section for more information on diodes (page 69).

Evaluation

Again there are three main problems with this circuit.

1) The circuit may not be powerful enough to drive the coil.

2) It is more expensive than the first solution. It uses two power sources.

3) It is still not very sensitive.

Despite these faults the sound level from the bell is much improved.

Design solution 3

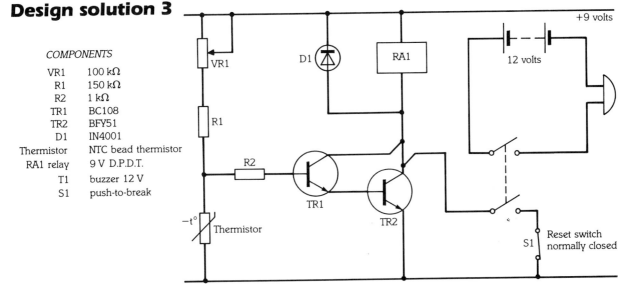

COMPONENTS

VR1	100 kΩ
R1	150 kΩ
R2	1 kΩ
TR1	BC108
TR2	BFY51
D1	IN4001
Thermistor	NTC bead thermistor
RA1 relay	9 V D.P.D.T.
T1	buzzer 12 V
S1	push-to-break

+9 volts

12 volts

Reset switch
normally closed

S1

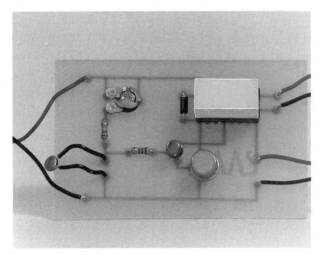

Design solution 3 on PCB

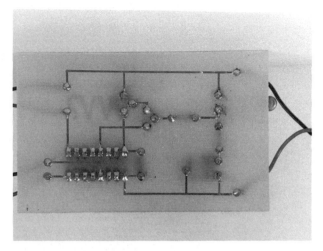

Underside of the PCB

This circuit differs from Design solution 2 in the following ways.

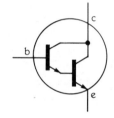

Darlington pair symbol

a) Transistors not only act as switches but they can be used to amplify the collector current in relationship to the base current. If two transistors are arranged in the formation shown in the circuit diagram the **current gain** is very large (see the research section on transistors, page 86). The two resistors together were able to drive motors and relays; they also make the circuit more sensitive.

These two transistors can be replaced by a power transistor such as a TIP141 which combines them inside one case.

This arrangement is referred to as a 'Darlington Pair'.

b) The relay will latch when operated. This means that if the contacts on the coil are energised the switch connections will remain in contact with each other even if the temperature sensing circuit switches off. In practical terms, the alarm, once activated, will continue to ring until it is turned off by the reset switch.

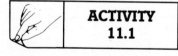

ACTIVITY 11.1

Assemble and test the last circuit using a TIP141, or use two alternative transistors.

ASSIGNMENT 11.1

1) Evaluate the new circuit (3) in terms of its use in the Garden Centre as a warning device. Can you anticipate any problems that may occur with this design in practice?

2) Propose and draw your own solutions to the problem. Use appropriate graphic techniques to sell your ideas.

CHAPTER 12

Simple timing circuits

The fridge door alarm was greeted with delight when it was first installed. However, because it operates each time the door is opened the black looks have returned.

Design brief

For peace and quiet you have decided to modify the alarm circuit so that it only operates after a fixed period of time.

Analysis/research

You need to investigate the amount of time a fridge door remains open for the average visit. This will give you some indication of what delay period you will require.

Timing is a very important concept in electronics and it can be achieved in many ways. Perhaps the simplest method available to the designer is to use a capacitor and resistor in series as a signal source for a transistor switch.

A capacitor stores electric charge. The amount of charge it can store is called its **capacitance** (C), and is measured in **farads** (symbol F). See the research section, Chapter 16, for more details on capacitors.

Symbols for capacitors

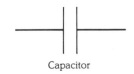

Capacitor

Old Symbol

Electrolytic (polarised) capacitor

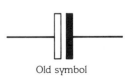

Old symbol

If a voltage is applied to a discharged capacitor a current will flow into it. It is then said to be *charging*. When it cannot receive any more charge the current will stop flowing. It is then said to be *fully charged*.

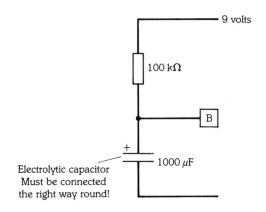

During the charging period the voltage at point B begins to rise. It is this property that can be used in a potential divider circuit to provide a time delay.

The component values given above would provide a delay of about 100 seconds. However, working out the time this circuit would take to switch on a transistor is not straightforward.

Capacitors only charge uniformly over the time taken to reach two-thirds of the supply voltage. This time is found by multiplying the resistance (ohms) by the capacitance (farads).

$$T \text{ (seconds)} = R \times C$$

How to calculate a time delay

1) Calculate the time taken for the capacitor to reach two-thirds of the supply voltage.

In the case of the circuit above this would be:

$$T \text{ (s)} = 100\,000 \times \left(\frac{1000}{1\,000\,000} \right)$$

Note that 1000 microfarads have been converted to 1000/100 000 farads.

$$T \text{ (s)} = 100\,000 \times 0.001$$
$$= 100 \text{ seconds}$$

2) Calculate the time taken to reach the switching voltage of a transistor.

If a transistor was connected to point B it would require approximately 0.6 volts to saturate.

If it takes 100 seconds to charge the capacitor to 6 volts then it should take 10 seconds to produce 0.6 volts at point B.

By increasing the size of the resistance to 1 megaohm ($1\,000\,000\,\Omega$ or 1 million ohms) the delay before the transistor can switch would increase to *about* 100 seconds. Check this by calculation.

Note: Very large value capacitors may not successfully provide a long time delay.

To discharge the capacitor quickly it needs to be shorted out by connecting its +ve side to earth or −ve rail (earthed).

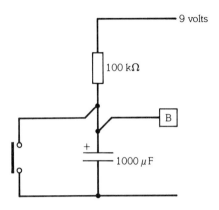

To protect the contacts of the switch from burning out when large value capacitors are used, a resistor connected in series with it will limit the current flow. This will also slow the rate of discharge.

In systems terms the following would be true:

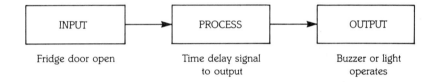

INPUT	PROCESS	OUTPUT
Fridge door open	Time delay signal to output	Buzzer or light operates

Design solution 1

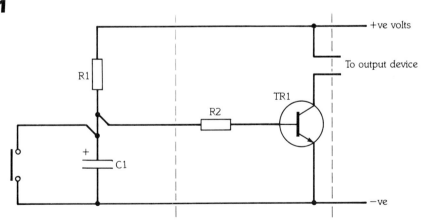

COMPONENTS

R1 $100\,k\Omega$
R2 $2\,k\Omega$
C1 $1000\,\mu F$
      $10\,V/16\,V$
TR1   BFY51

When the fridge door is closed the contacts on the switch also remain closed. This keeps the capacitor in a discharged state. When the door is opened the switch contacts are broken. The greatest drop in potential difference occurs across the resistor but as the capacitor begins to charge the signal voltage will increase until it switches on the transistor.

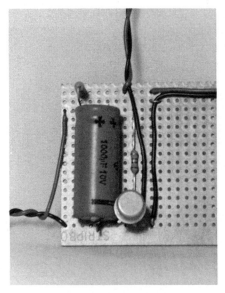

Timing circuit on Veroboard   Underside of Veroboard

ASSIGNMENT 12.1

Calculate the values of the components for the time delay you require.

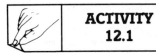

ACTIVITY 12.1

1) Assemble and test the circuit.

2) Evaluate its performance. What factors do you think will make the circuit behave differently from the results you obtained by calculation?

3) How can the circuit be fine tuned to give an accurate time delay? (*Hint:* See the temperature sensing circuits in Chapter 11).

CHAPTER 13

555 Timer monostable

Design problem

On a visit to a local Sheltered Home for the elderly, your attention is drawn to a problem that some of the residents have in operating certain equipment. The device used to summon help is heavily criticised. The system works, but residents who have limited movement in their hands find difficulty in pushing the alarm switch when they need help urgently.

Design brief

You have been asked to investigate the problem above and provide a solution that can be constructed easily and evaluated by the people who have to use it.

Research/analysis

The existing system (which is very old!) needs to be explained.

Residents, who may require instant help, have their rooms wired into the alarm system. This consists of a toggle switch set into the wall, which is connected to a bell and a light in the reception area.

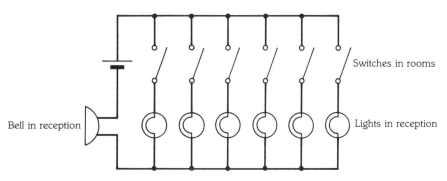

Bell in reception   Switches in rooms

                                                                     Lights in reception

The warden can identify the room where the alarm has been operated because the bell rings in reception and a light shows where the alarm switch has been activated.

You need to devise a questionnaire that will help to determine what is wrong with the existing system. It should involve both staff and residents.

What do you think this questionnaire would reveal?

The range of disabilities that affect movement and co-ordination (e.g. poor eyesight, Parkinson's disease, arthritis) will need to be investigated.

In systems terms the following should be true:

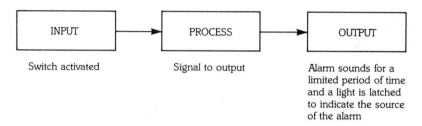

INPUT	PROCESS	OUTPUT
Switch activated	Signal to output	Alarm sounds for a limited period of time and a light is latched to indicate the source of the alarm

Design solution 1

There are many alarm systems that could be used, for example a light-activated switch using an LDR, but the solution presented below employs an **integrated circuit** or **IC**. Read about ICs in the research section, Chapter 16. It is very important that you do this before continuing.

A very useful IC is a 555 timer chip. This comes in an 8-pin DIL (dual in line) package that contains 25 transistors, 2 diodes and 16 resistors inside a case which measures about 10 mm × 6 mm.

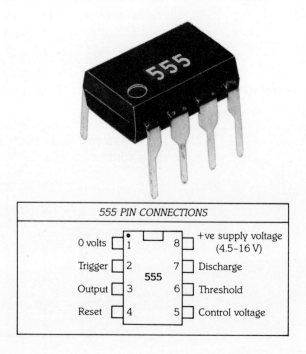

555 PIN CONNECTIONS

0 volts	1	8	+ve supply voltage (4.5–16 V)
Trigger	2	7	Discharge
Output	3	6	Threshold
Reset	4	5	Control voltage

A useful circuit using the 555 timer is drawn below.

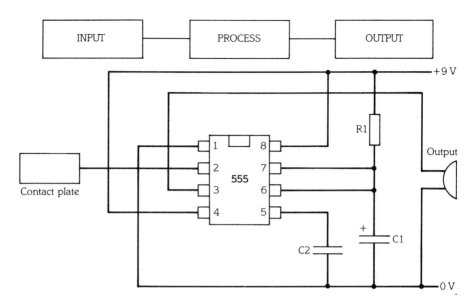

COMPONENTS

R1   10 kΩ
C1   220 μF 10 V
C2   0.1 μF

It is not necessary for you to have a detailed knowledge of how the chip works.

You need to understand the following: that when the input pin 2 is touched your body allows the voltage at this point to drop to below ⅓ of the supply voltage. A high output voltage is produced at pin 3 when this happens. This output can be used to drive an electromechanical device or output transducer such as a bell or light.

The contact plate can be made of any conducting material and can be as large as you want. It has no moving parts. This is a particularly useful feature in relationship to the brief.

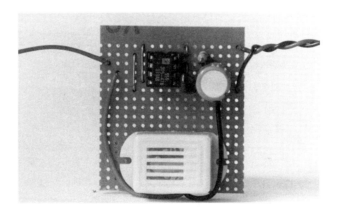

Design solution 1 on Veroboard

If the input and output pulse were represented pictorially they would look like the drawings below.

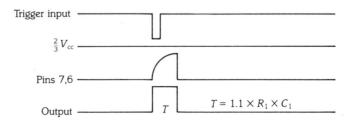

$$T = 1.1 \times R_1 \times C_1$$

There are two things about the input pulse that must be noted:
a) it must be shorter in duration than the output pulse and
b) the device is triggered by the input voltage suddenly dropping.
   This type of trigger occurs on a **negative going edge**.

The 555 timer, in this circuit will operate in a **monostable** form. In practical terms this means that when the contact plate is touched the light or bell connected to the output will switch on for a certain period of time and then turn off.

The time period for which the output remains high can be altered by changing the values of the resistor and/or capacitor in series. To calculate the time delay we use the equation:

$$T = 1.1 \times R \text{ (megaohms)} \times C \text{ (microfarads)}$$

If we use the values from the circuit above then

$$T = 1.1 \times \frac{100\,000}{1\,000\,000} \times 2.2 = 0.242 \text{ Hz (beats per second)}$$

i.e. 1 pulse which lasts for approximately 4 seconds.

In terms of the design brief this equation is very useful. It will enable you to determine how long you want the bell to operate before the circuit resets.

Evaluation

The circuit was very sensitive. It produced an output pulse as soon as it was touched. Once the time period had passed, the circuit reset and was ready to operate again.

If the reception area was empty during this period then no record of the request for help would be available. The values of R and C could be changed to give a longer output time. Whilst this would solve the initial problem it is not a satisfactory answer.

Design solution 2

If you remove the timing resistor from the previous circuit, the 555 chip will, in effect, *latch*. This means that it will continue to produce an output signal until it is manually reset. The chip is now in a **bi-stable** configuration.

COMPONENTS

C1, C2   0.1 μF ceramic
S1   push-to-make

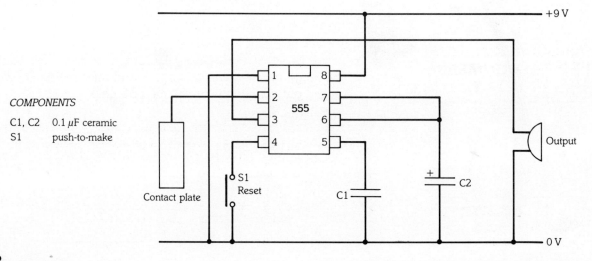

By combining Design solution 1 and the circuit drawn on page 48, a design can be produced that will turn on a buzzer for a limited period of time. The light will remain latched until it is manually reset.

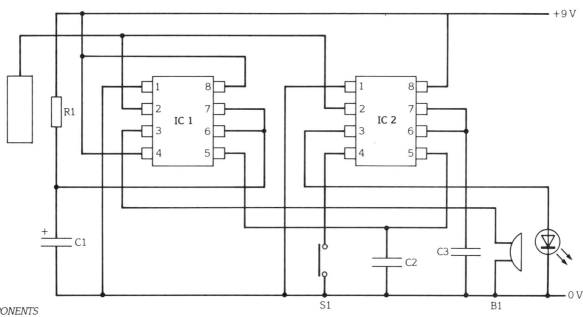

COMPONENTS

IC1, IC2	555	C1	$10\,\mu F$ 25 V	B1	9 V buzzer	LED
R1	$100\,k\Omega$	C2, C3	$0.1\,\mu F$ disc	S1	push-to-make	

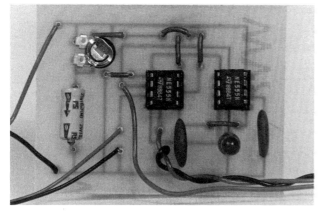

Design solution 2 on PCB

IC1 acts as the monostable switch with an output to the buzzer and IC2 acts as the latch with an output to the LED. S1 is the reset switch for the latch circuit.

ASSIGNMENT 13.1

1) Two 555s can be obtained in a single package called a 556. Look at manufacturers' or suppliers' catalogues and information sheets to find out the pin configurations for the 556 chip.

2) Redraw the circuit diagram shown above, replacing the two 555s with one 556 chip. Design a component layout for both circuits that you could make.

ACTIVITY 13.1

Decide which circuit would be the most appropriate to use. Make the circuit, test it and evaluate it in terms of the original brief.

555 Timer astable

| Design problem | As part of a community project your school has been asked to restore a number of toys for a children's play group. An old bicycle, suitable for a 4 to 6 year old, is amongst the items delivered to the school. It needs to be cleaned and repainted before it can be used. Other features are required to make it more appealing to the modern child. |

Design brief

Members of your group are investigating ways in which the bike can be made to look more fashionable, but you have been asked to design and make an electronic device that will make it more attractive.

Research/analysis

It is important to establish a theme or style for the restoration of the bike.

Any solution must be easy to construct and maintain.

The device must be robust. If you observe any group of young children using bicycles you will find that they don't always take the greatest care of their machines.

The cheapest solution must be used. There is no additional money available to fund this restoration.

The device must be easy to operate.

Sound and/or light are two features which are easily controlled through electronic circuits.

In previous chapters we have used a monostable or bistable switch to control light or sound.

By introducing the **astable** switch the range of solutions that we can offer to solve this design problem is greatly increased. An astable switch is a device that continually flips between two states. In practical terms this could mean that a light flashes on and off repeatedly. A 555 timer can be configured to produce an astable output pulse.

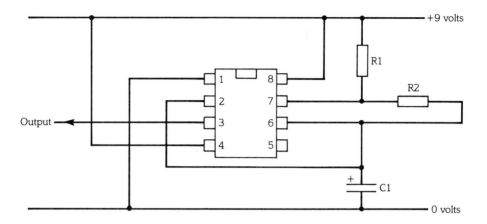

If we were to represent the input and output pulses in pictorial form they would look like this:

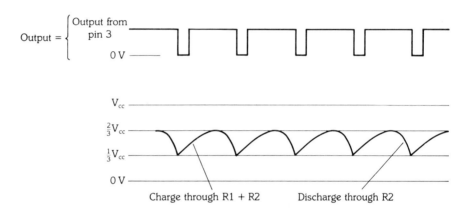

The 555 in this configuration can be called a **pulse generator** or **oscillator**. The rate at which the device oscillates can be altered by adjusting the values of R_1, R_2 and C_1. The frequency of oscillation (f) can be worked out by using the equation:

$$f = \frac{1.44}{(R_1 + 2 \times R_2) \times C}$$

Note that C is measured in microfarads and R in megaohms.

If R_1 = 10 kΩ, R_2 = 68 kΩ and C = 10 µF

Then

$$f = \frac{1.44}{(0.01 + 2 \times 0.068) \times 10}$$

$$f = \frac{1.44}{1.46}$$

$$f = 0.98 \text{ Hz}$$

(approximately 1 beat per second)

51

In systems terms the following should be true:

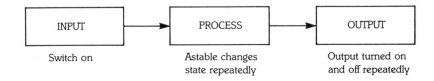

INPUT	PROCESS	OUTPUT
Switch on	Astable changes state repeatedly	Output turned on and off repeatedly

Design solution 1

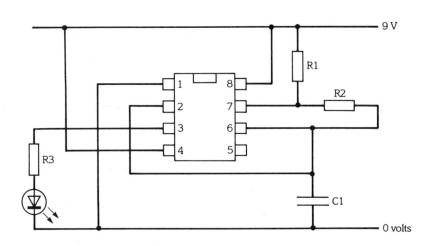

You can make the circuit more interesting by adding another light:

COMPONENTS

IC1	555
R1	1 kΩ
R2	10 kΩ
R3	330 Ω
R4	330 Ω
C1	10 µF 25 V

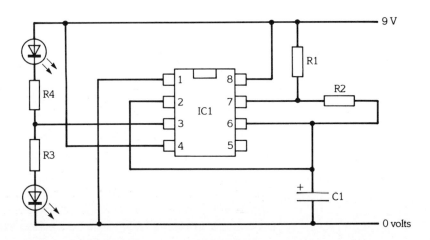

Design solution 1 on PCB

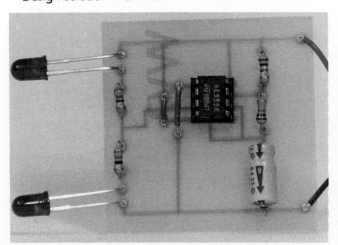

Further lights can be added in the following way:

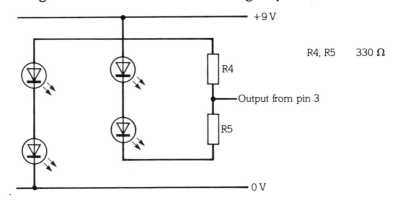

R4, R5   330 Ω

Two LEDs are on when the other two are off.

Design solution 2

By adding another chip to the 555 we can make an LED sequencer or 'chaser'. You do not need to understand very much about this IC (4017B) in order to use it. But you do need to know that when it is wired in the configuration shown below, the LEDs connected to pins 1 to 11 will each light up in sequence. The process will continually repeat itself until the circuit is disconnected from the power supply.

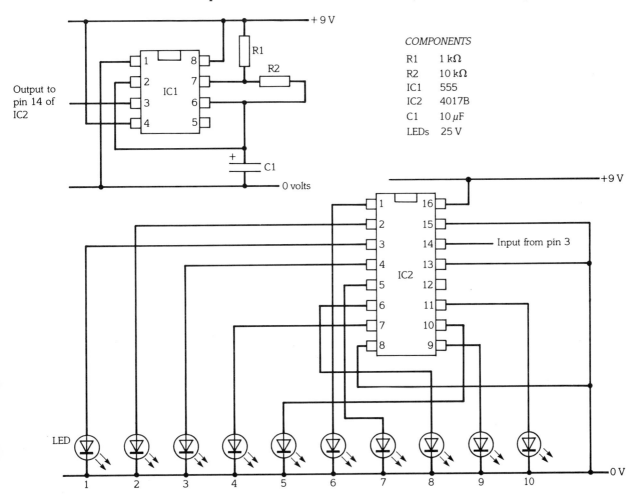

COMPONENTS

R1	1 kΩ
R2	10 kΩ
IC1	555
IC2	4017B
C1	10 μF
LEDs	25 V

The LEDs must be connected in the order shown above to create the sequence or 'chaser' effect, but they can be arranged in any shape or pattern.

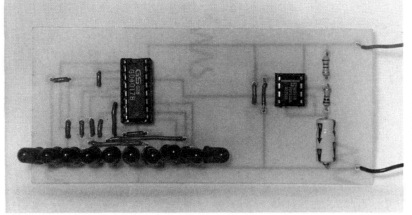

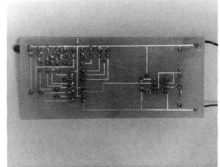

Design solution 2 on PCB   Underside of the PCB

Design solution 3

If the astable output pin 3 is connected to a capacitor and speaker in series a sound will be produced.

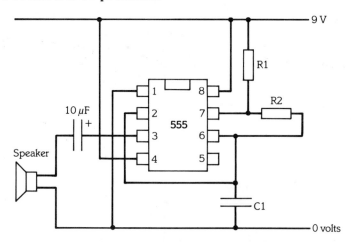

The pitch of the sound can be varied by changing the values of R_1, R_2 and C_1.

Two 555 timers can be used to produce a siren effect.

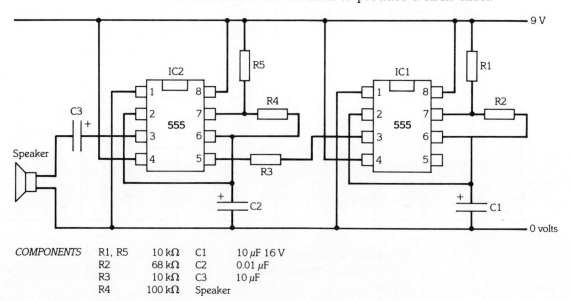

COMPONENTS	R1, R5	10 kΩ	C1	10 μF 16 V
	R2	68 kΩ	C2	0.01 μF
	R3	10 kΩ	C3	10 μF
	R4	100 kΩ	Speaker	

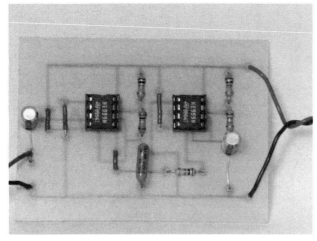

Design solution 3 on PCB

Underside of the PCB

Normally the frequency of an astable output is affected by the combination of external resistors and capacitors. It can also be altered by changing the control voltage at pin 5. In this circuit IC1 changes the voltage to pin 5 of IC2, producing the siren-like output.

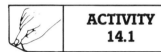

ACTIVITY 14.1

1) Modify the last circuit so that the two 555 ICs are replaced by a 556. Draw your solution on paper.

2) Compare the circuits and decide which would be the most suitable design to complete the brief.

ASSIGNMENT 14.1

Produce a completed circuit, together with the appropriate paperwork to support your design. Evaluate the performance of your completed device against those produced by other members of your class.

Operational amplifiers 741 series

Design problem

Your next-door neighbour is a very active 70-year-old who enjoys life to the full. He has been a family friend for as long as you can remember. Recently his sight has deteriorated to the point where he is almost blind. Despite having a home help he refuses to give up doing as much for himself as he can.

One of his great pleasures in life is having a deep, soothing bath before retiring to bed. On occasions, he has overfilled the bath.

Design brief

In order to resolve this problem you are going to design and make an alarm that will sound when the bath water reaches a pre-determined level.

Research/analysis

You need to decide at what depth of water the alarm should be triggered.

A battery powered solution is necessary because of the danger present when water and electricity are combined.

The physical position of the alarm itself could be either inside or outside the bathroom. You need to consider the advantages and disadvantages of either site.

Any design solution must be cheap to make.

You are going to have to pay for the components yourself and your financial situation is *precarious*.

You have already experienced alarm circuits that use a transistor as a switch. Another discrete component that can be used in a similar fashion is called an **operational amplifier**.

A 741, which is a typical operational amplifier, is available in a single 8-pin DIL package. It is a very versatile chip that can be used in many situations where a small signal needs to be amplified. The IC contains 20 transistors, 11 resistors and 1 capacitor. It was originally developed to solve mathematical problems. This diagram shows the connections.

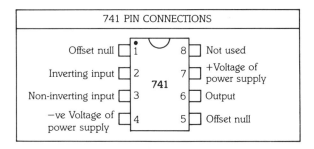

The symbol for an operational amplifier (op amp) is drawn in the following way:

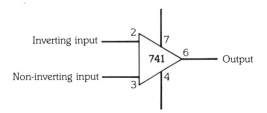

A 741 op amp has two inputs and one output. The *non-inverting* input can be marked + and the *inverting* input can be marked −.

The circuit is normally operated from two power supplies at the same time. One provides a positive voltage (and earth) and the other provides a negative voltage (and earth). This is referred to as a dual voltage, balanced supply. The earth rail is common to both the input and output.

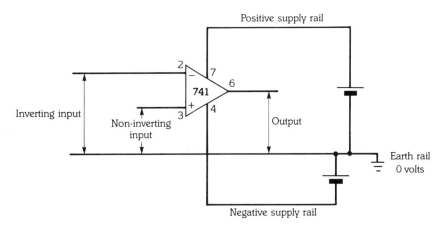

Take care not to confuse inverting and non-inverting input signs with the voltage supply signs.

Comparator circuits

A comparator is a circuit that continuously checks two voltages and compares one against the other.

One voltage is called the reference voltage (V_{ref}), the other is called the input voltage (V_{in}). When the input voltage rises above or falls below V_{ref}, the output of the comparator changes states. When V_{in} is higher than V_{ref} by a few microvolts the output switches from low to high.

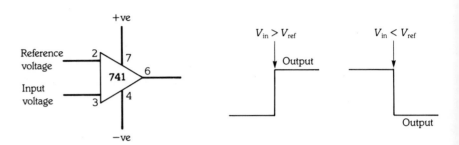

When V_{in} is lower than V_{ref} by a few microvolts the output switches from high to low.

When V_{in} equals V_{ref} (which is very rare) the output will be 0 volts.

By earthing the positive terminal and using the negative terminal as an input the 741 functions as an inverting d.c. amplifier.

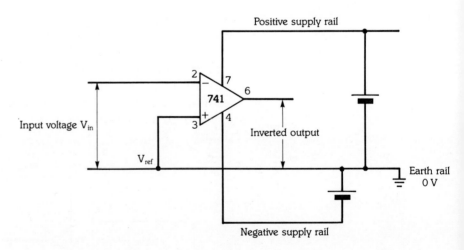

If the chip is configured in either the inverting or non-inverting state it is **open looped** (without feedback). This will provide a voltage gain of about 100 000 :1. This means that if the non-inverting terminal was 0.0001 V higher than the inverting terminal, then the output could be nearly as high as the supply voltage. *(The output cannot exceed the supply voltage.)*

Each individual IC has its own slightly different characteristics and so the actual gain will be more difficult to predict.

A far more useful way of employing the op amp is to use it in a **closed loop** (negative feedback) mode.

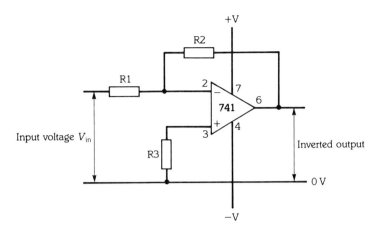

The feedback resistor R_2 sends some of the amplified signal from the output back into the inverting input. This reduces the size of the input signal and thereby reduces the amplification. The gain of the circuit is calculated by the equation:

$$\text{Gain} = \frac{R_2}{R_1}$$

Op amps generally need two power supplies to work satisfactorily. There are occasions when this is not practical. The circuit drawn below is an example of how a single power supply can provide the appropriate voltages.

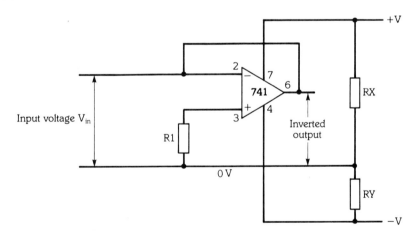

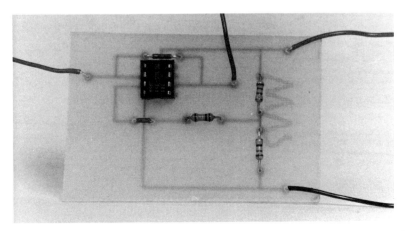

The above circuit on PCB

The values of R_X and R_Y must be calculated with care. The current flowing through them must be greater than the peak output current taken from the op amp.

Design solution 1

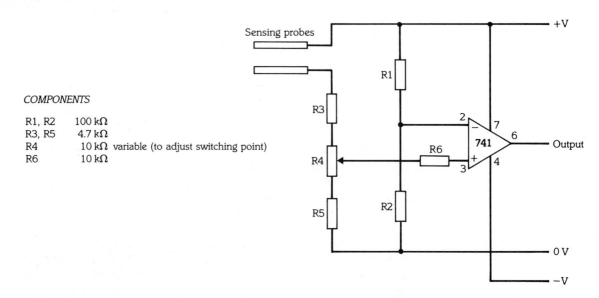

COMPONENTS

R1, R2	100 kΩ
R3, R5	4.7 kΩ
R4	10 kΩ variable (to adjust switching point)
R6	10 kΩ

If the probes are dry the input to pin 2 will be more positive than that of pin 3. The output from the op amp in this circumstance will be *low*, (non-inverting output).

If water comes into contact with the probes the voltage on pin 3 will begin to rise. When it is slightly above the voltage level of pin 2 the op amp will change state — the output will go *high*.

The output can be connected to a transistor-controlled relay switch that can be used to operate a bell or buzzer (see Chapter 10).

To use this circuit for other switching/sensing situations the probes (and R_4) can be replaced by such devices as LDRs, thermistors or resistor/capacitor networks for time delays. Positive feedback between pin 6 and pin 3 (connected by a resistor) will cause a sudden switching action.

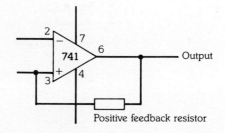

Positive feedback resistor

The use of a 741 in this way produces a sensitive switching circuit.

Design solution 2

The basic circuit shown below enables the op amp to act as a combined voltage comparator and astable switch ('relaxation oscillator').

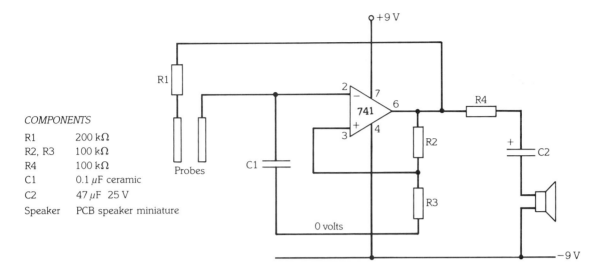

COMPONENTS

R1	200 kΩ
R2, R3	100 kΩ
R4	100 kΩ
C1	0.1 µF ceramic
C2	47 µF 25 V
Speaker	PCB speaker miniature

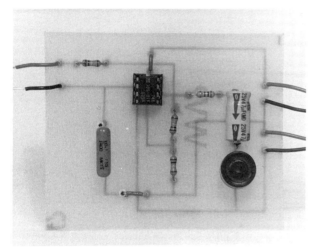

Design solution 2 on PCB

Underside of the PCB

If the output from pin 6 is high, half of this voltage is sent to pin 3 (through the potential divider R_2/R_3 in a feedback loop). This will keep pin 3 more positive than pin 2. A second feedback loop (via the probes) starts the capacitor C_1 charging and gradually makes pin 2 more positive than pin 3. This will cause the op amp to switch to a low output.

As time passes pin 2 will eventually become more negative than pin 3. The output from the op amp will then be high. This process continually repeats itself until externally stopped. This causes the speaker to produce a tone.

By changing the values of R_1 to R_4 or (C_1) the frequency of the 'relaxation' oscillator can be changed. If R_1 is removed, oscillation will stop.

This circuit can also be used in many different applications by using transducers such as LDRs, etc.

Evaluation

The circuit was very sensitive, but once it was triggered it went on and on . . . and on!! It requires an on/off switch. Another problem was that condensation formed on the side of the bath (which caused false alarms). The probes were moved a little way away from the side of the bath to insulate them.

	ASSIGNMENT 15.1

Modify the existing circuit so that it will produce a rise in pitch as the water level increases. There are many ways of doing this, some cheaper than others. Cost your solutions before ordering the parts and commencing work.

	ACTIVITY 15.1

1) Design, build and test your circuit.

2) Write an evaluation of it.

3) Package and market your solution as if it were to be sold through a high street chain of stores.

Capacitors

Capacitors are made of two conducting plates that are separated by an insulating material called a dielectric. When connected to the terminals of a d.c. power supply the plate attached to the positive rail will try to absorb electrons from the plate linked to the negative rail. The dielectric stops the electrons from reaching the positive plate. In this way a capacitor can store electrical energy. In other words it can behave in a similar way to a battery, although it will not conduct a d.c. current.

The energy stored in a capacitor is measured in **farads** (F), which is a very large unit. Most circuits that you will use will involve capacitors that have a value much smaller than 1 farad.

Below is a list of how the farad is subdivided into smaller units.

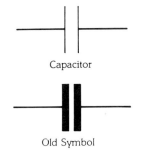

Capacitor

	Symbol	Factor
1 farad = 1000 millifarads	mF	10^{-3}
1 farad = 1 000 000 microfarads	μF	10^{-6}
1 farad = 1 000 000 000 nanofarads	nF	10^{-9}
1 farad = 1 000 000 000 000 picofarads	pF	10^{-12}

Old Symbol

There are two main types of capacitor: polarised and unpolarised. A polarised (electrolytic) capacitor has one side marked '+', and you must be careful to connect it the correct way round in a d.c. circuit. Unpolarised capacitors can be connected either way round.

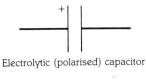

Electrolytic (polarised) capacitor

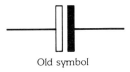

Old symbol

Symbols

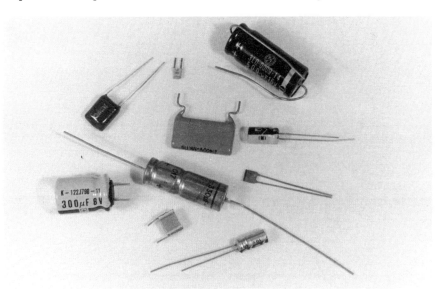

Capacitors come in all shapes and sizes

Circuit boards

In the examples shown below the circuit to be used is this:

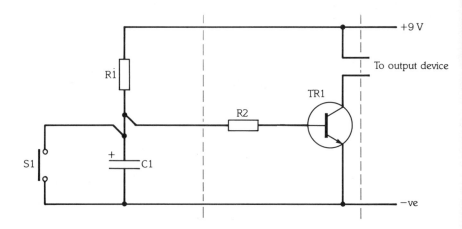

Matrix board

Matrix board is made out of an insulating material that has a series of holes drilled in it 0.1 inch apart. Pins are force fitted into the holes. The circuit components and connecting leads are soldered to the pins.

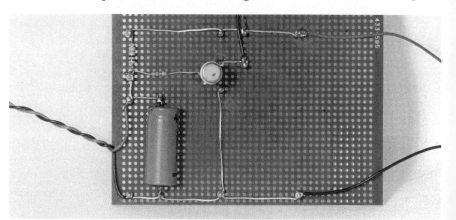

a) Identify components.

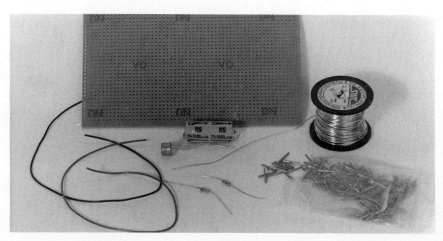

b) Measure sizes (spacing of connecting leads).

c) Use a sheet of 0.1 inch graph paper (to match the spacing of the holes). Transfer the circuit diagram onto this paper, taking into account the sizes of the components. This produces a master 'plan'.

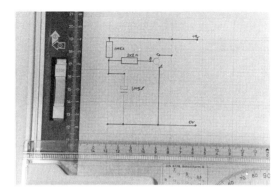

d) Indicate where the connecting pins will be placed (external wires).

e) Cut the matrix board to size using a junior hacksaw and smooth the edges with a fine file.

f) Insert pins in position using the graph paper 'plan' as a guide.

g) Tin all the pins on the board (see 'Soldering').

h) Solder any plain and insulated connecting wire onto the pins. (It helps if the wire is wrapped around the pin to hold it in place before soldering.) Multi-stranded wire will need to be tinned before doing this.

i) Solder all components into position but leave any semiconductors like diodes and transistors until last.

j) Use crocodile clips fastened onto each lead of the transistor or diode when soldering. They form a heat sink and help to avoid overheating the component.

k) Check and test the circuit.

Veroboard

Veroboard is made out of an insulating material that has a series of holes drilled in it 0.1 inch apart. The reverse side of the board is coated with conducting tracks. The circuit components and connecting leads are placed through the holes and soldered onto the copper track. Breaks are cut in the track where needed.

The circuit being constructed here is the transistor switching circuit from Chapter 10.

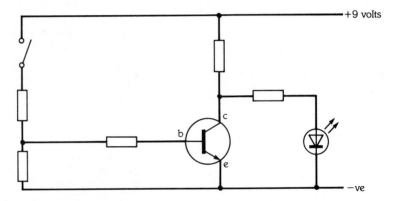

Breaks are cut in the copper tracks with a special tool where connections are not wanted

a) Identify components.

b) Measure sizes (spacing of connecting leads).

c) Use a sheet of 0.1 inch graph paper (to match the spacing of the holes). Transfer the circuit diagram onto this paper taking into account the sizes of the components. This produces a master 'plan'.

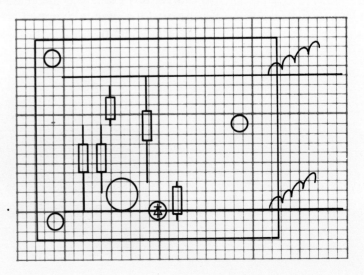

d) Indicate where the components and breaks in the track will be placed (external wires).

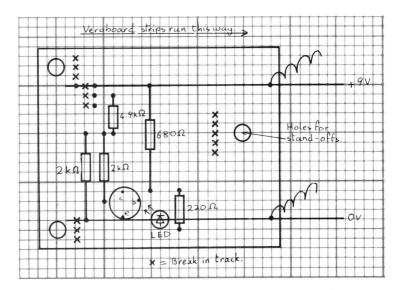

e) Cut the Veroboard to size using a junior hacksaw and smooth the edges with a fine file.

f) Insert the components in position using the graph paper 'plan' as a guide.

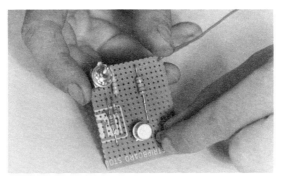

g) Solder all components into position but leave any semiconductors like diodes and transistors until last.

h) Use crocodile clips fastened onto each lead of the transistor or diode when soldering. They form a heat sink and help to avoid overheating the component.

i) Solder any externally required wires onto the board.

j) Check and test the circuit.

PCB production

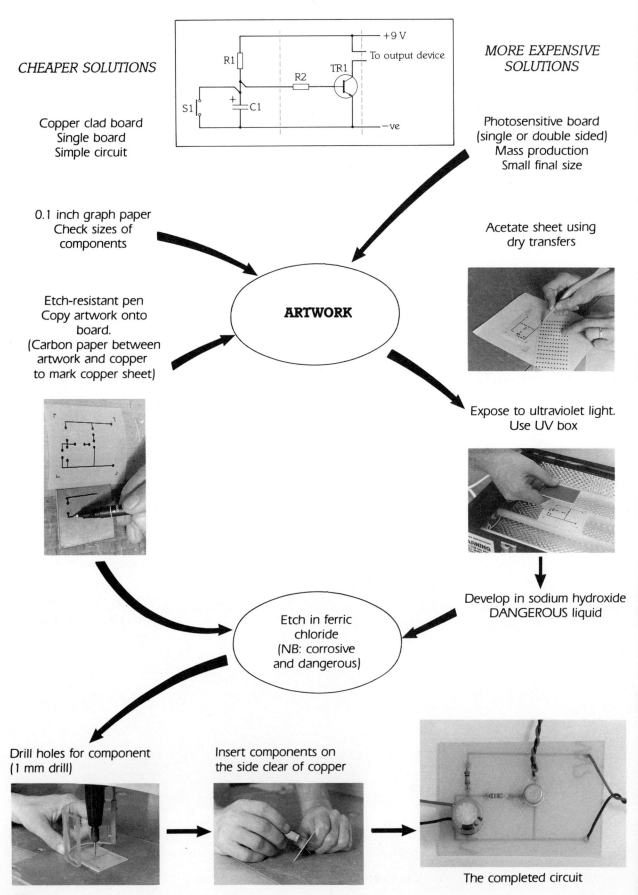

CHEAPER SOLUTIONS

Copper clad board
Single board
Simple circuit

+9 V
To output device
R1
R2
TR1
S1
+
C1
−ve

MORE EXPENSIVE
SOLUTIONS

Photosensitive board
(single or double sided)
Mass production
Small final size

0.1 inch graph paper
Check sizes of
components

Acetate sheet using
dry transfers

ARTWORK

Etch-resistant pen
Copy artwork onto
board.
(Carbon paper between
artwork and copper
to mark copper sheet)

Expose to ultraviolet light.
Use UV box

Develop in sodium hydroxide
DANGEROUS liquid

Etch in ferric
chloride
(NB: corrosive
and dangerous)

Drill holes for component
(1 mm drill)

Insert components on
the side clear of copper

The completed circuit

Diodes

Diodes are semiconductors. They conduct electricity in one direction only. The positive terminal is called the anode, the negative is called the cathode.

Junction diodes

Junction diodes are used for voltage rectification and to protect other components from damaging high voltages. For example, they can be used across the terminals of a relay (see page 39).

Diode (new symbol)   Diode (old symbol)

Light emitting diode

The light emitting diode (LED) is a junction diode that glows when it conducts electricity. Most LEDs are used as indicators in devices such as tape recorders and radios. They can be bought in a wide variety of shapes, colours and arrangements. They can also have a small IC inside them that will cause the diode to flash on and off.

Symbol   Cathode (−ve)   Anode (+ve)

Two types of LED

Fault finding

One of the most frustrating things about electronics is when a circuit does not work. Discovering the reason why the circuit does not operate is very important. To do this successfully you must work systematically and thoroughly.

Check that:

1) all the components are the right ones and have been put in the appropriate places,
2) the components are the correct way round, e.g. diodes and transistors,
3) all the soldered and mechanical joints are making good electrical contact,
4) all wires are correctly placed,
5) the tracks on PCB and stripboard circuits do not have breaks in them,
6) stripboard is correctly cut where needed.
7) Use a multimeter to check that semiconductor devices have not been overheated whilst being soldered into position.
   Note: Some ICs can be damaged by handling.
8) Check that the voltage and current readings for the circuit are what you expect or calculate (use a multimeter).

It is rare for new components to fail. Faulty circuits are normally the result of poor connections.

If you cannot find a fault in a circuit when you have been through this process, ask someone else to check it for you.

Integrated circuits

An 8-pin DIL integrated circuit

ICs represent a very important development in the evolution of electronics. These discrete devices, often called 'chips', are manufactured from thin slices of silicon. Complex circuits made up of many components are created on a very small silicon wafer and encapsulated in a moulded block of plastic. The circuit is connected to external components by a series of pins that extend outside the encapsulating plastic.

Integrated circuits are packaged in a standard format. In the smaller sizes the connecting pins are spaced every 0.1 inch along the side of the package, with 0.3 inch between the sides.

A socket for a 16-pin DIL integrated circuit

DIL packages can come in 4, 8, 14, 16, 18, 20, 24, 28 or 40 pin packages. As ICs are often damaged by heat they are inserted into a socket which has been first soldered into position ready to receive the DIL encapsulated circuit. This also allows a damaged integrated circuit to be quickly removed and replaced.

When using an IC it is very important to know

a) what it will do,
b) what the operating restrictions are (in terms of voltage, etc.),
c) what the pin configuration is. This is usually determined by the position of pin 1. When looking at the chip from above, pin 1 is to the left of the dot or notch.

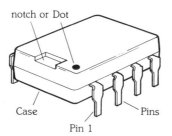

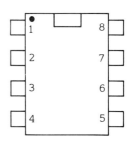

Multimeters

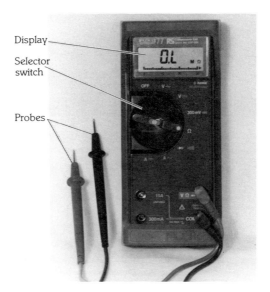

Finding out what values of voltage and/or current are present in a circuit is a very important part of electronics. Modern digital multimeters make this a very easy thing to do. There are many varieties on the market and you should read the makers' instructions before using them. They are relatively cheap and offer many features, such as the ability to measure voltage, current, resistance, capacitance and the gain h_{fe} of a transistor.

It is important to remember that when measuring current the multimeter is connected *in series* with the part of the circuit being tested.

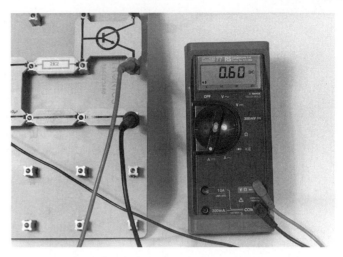

Measuring current

When measuring voltage the multimeter is connected *in parallel* with the component being tested.

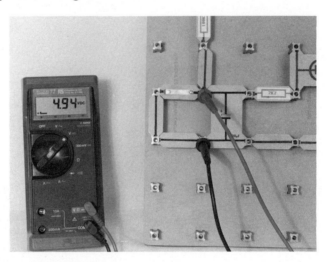

Measuring voltage

When measuring resistance there must be no external power supply connected to the device being tested.

Ohm's law

The voltage (V), resistance (R) and current (I) in a circuit are related. If two of these three values are known, the third can be calculated from the equation:

$$V = I \times R$$

where V is in volts, I in amps and R in ohms.
This is known as **Ohm's law.**

The formula can be rearranged in the following ways:

$$V = I \times R \qquad I = \frac{V}{R} \qquad R = \frac{V}{I}$$

Potential divider calculations

In the circuit on page 23 we saw that

$$\text{Voltage at point B} (V_{\text{out}}) = \text{Voltage at point C } (V_{\text{in}}) \times \frac{R_2}{(R_1 + R_2)}$$

We can use the equation to find out what value of R_2 is required to produce a V_{out} of 6 V if R_1 is 100 Ω. By inserting the known values in the equation we have

$$6 = 9 \times \frac{R_2}{100 + R_2}$$

$$\frac{6}{9} = \frac{R_2}{100 + R_2}$$

Inverting the equation we get

$$\frac{9}{6} = \frac{100 + R_2}{R_2}$$

Working out both sides of the equation:

$$1.5 = \frac{100}{R_2} + 1$$

Transferring the 1 from right to left:

$$1.5 - 1 = \frac{100}{R_2}$$

and then subtracting:

$$0.5 = \frac{100}{R_2}$$

Re-arranging the equation:

$$R_2 = \frac{100}{0.5}$$

we get the answer:

$$R_2 = 200 \ \Omega$$

Prototyping

There are many different ways of producing a prototype of your circuit design. Some of these involve a commercial kit of assembled parts of a circuit, others use components that are mounted on a special board.

These are some examples of commercially available prototyping equipment which have been used to put the following circuit together.

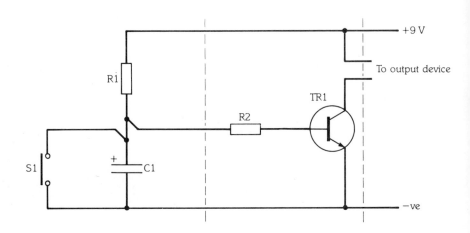

Danum-trent

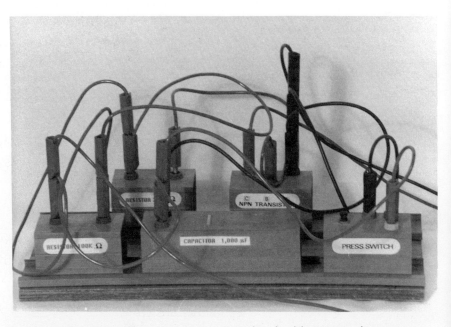

Plug-in leads connect the components together in this prototyping system to make the above circuit

Locktronics

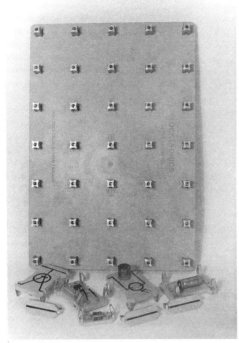

Components and baseboard

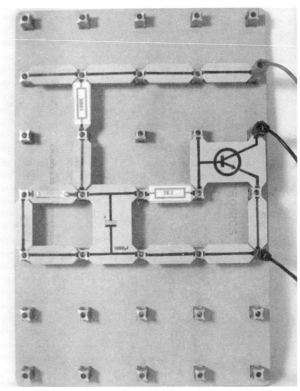

The circuit made up using the Locktronics system

Breadboard

The underside of a
breadboard

All the holes in this row are connected
to each other inside the board

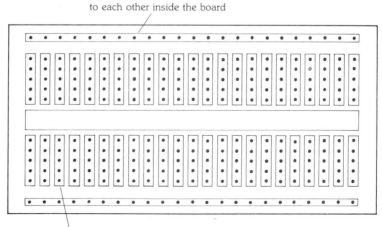

The arrangement of the
connecting strips on the
underside of the breadboard

The five holes in this half column are
connected to each other inside the board

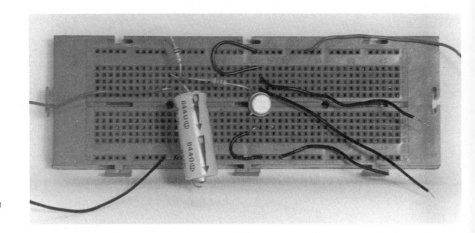

The same circuit made up on a breadboard

Resistors

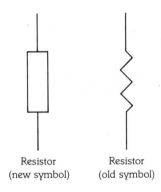

Resistor (new symbol)

Resistor (old symbol)

The unit of resistance is the ohm, represented by the symbol Ω — 'omega'.

The approved symbol for fixed resistors and the symbol that used to be used are shown on the left.

The most common type of resistor is the carbon film resistor. Other types are carbon composition, metal oxide and wirewound resistors.

The value of a fixed resistor is written as a colour code printed in rings around the body of the resistor. Resistors often have very high values. All the information is contained in the colour code.

THE RESISTOR COLOUR CODE

Number	Colour
0	Black
1	Brown
2	Red
3	Orange
4	Yellow
5	Green
6	Blue
7	Violet
8	Grey
9	White

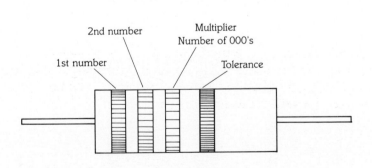

Remember, the rings are read as: 1st number, 2nd number, number of zeros.

If the colours are   Brown Black Brown
the resistor value is: 1   0   0   = 100 Ω or 100R

If the colours are   Yellow Violet Orange
the resistor value is: 4   7   000   = 47 000 Ω or 47K

Note the use of R and K to show where the decimal point should be in a resistance value.

The accuracy of a resistor is indicated by its **tolerance**. For example, a 1000 Ω resistor with a tolerance of ±10% would have a value that lies between 900 Ω and 1100 Ω.

Tolerance can be shown as a fourth band on a resistor or as a letter when written.

Gold band or 'J'   ± 5%
Silver band or 'K'   ± 10%
No band or 'M'   ± 20%

The flow of electricity through a conductor causes heat to be generated in it. The **power rating** is the maximum amount of power that can be passed through a resistor without it overheating and being damaged.

When a conductor heats up, its resistance normally decreases. The **stability** of a resistor is its ability to keep a constant value despite changes in temperature.

Factors that must be considered when choosing a resistor are:

1) value
2) type
3) physical size
4) tolerance
5) power rating
6) stability
7) price

Variable resistors

Variable resistors (or **potentiometers**) are used when a changing resistance value is needed in a circuit. Depending on the way in which it is connected, the same component could be a potential divider or a variable resistor.

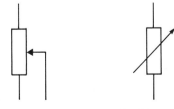

Symbols

Potential divider   Variable resistor

There are two forms of variable resistor, the variable resistor and a preset resistor. Both are available in rotary or linear designs.

Four designs of rotary variable resistor

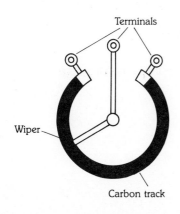

The track of the potentiometer can be made to be **linear** or **logarithmic**. With a linear potentiometer the resistance increases steadily as the wiper turns. Logarithmic tracks start with a small resistance and then the resistance increases rapidly as the wiper approaches the end of the track. Logarithmic potentiometers are used with audio systems.

The variable resistor is controlled manually but there are resistors that react automatically to light, heat and pressure.

Sensing circuits use potential divider networks. The potential divider in a sensing circuit is made from a light dependent resistor and a variable resistor. The variable resistor allows the circuit to be tuned so that the transistor can be operated when different light levels are falling on the LDR.

Soldering

Before a component is put into position ready for soldering, the parts to be soldered must be clean. Most commercially supplied components are precleaned and tinned (already coated in a thin layer of solder). It is better if the leads are cut to approximate length before insertion into the matrix board or PCB.

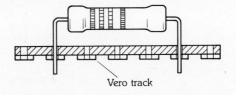

Vero track

Once the component is in place and physically held in position by bending the leads, it is ready to be soldered. The board and component are turned over ready for soldering.

Solder is a precise mixture of lead and tin that will chemically join with copper to provide a strong and conductive link. This is produced in wire form with small cores of flux running through it, as shown below.

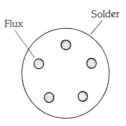

Soldering techniques

1) Tin any untreated wires.

2) Bend component leads and fit into place.

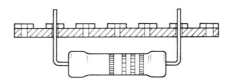

3) Apply heat to component and copper track.

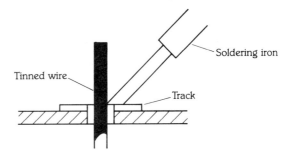

4) Melt solder onto preheated surfaces.

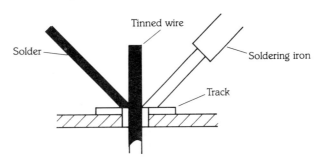

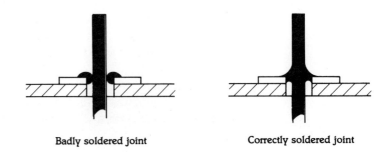

Badly soldered joint   Correctly soldered joint

Do not hold the component with your fingers.

Avoid overheating components, especially semiconductors. Transistors and IC sockets are available that can be soldered onto a board. The components can then be pushed into the sockets, thus avoiding the need to heat the device directly.

Switches

Switches are used to break a connection in a circuit. They can be used to either make or break a connection when they are operated. The most common forms of switch are the push switch and the toggle switch.

Push (*left*) and toggle (*right*) switches

The two symbols on the top line are for push-to-make and push-to-break switches:

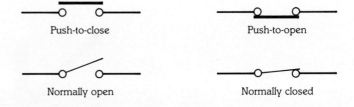

Push-to-close   Push-to-open

Normally open   Normally closed

The lower set of symbols are for 'normally open' and 'normally closed' toggle or reed switches.

For more complicated circuits, and when more than one circuit needs to be controlled, different kinds of switch may be used.

The normally open/normally closed type of switch is called a single-pole single-throw switch. This is shortened to S.P.S.T. It is used to connect and disconnect a single wire in a circuit. It is often used for turning the circuit on and off.

S.P.S.T. toggle switch

When a switch is used as an 'OR' gate to change over connections, i.e. to select one of two possible connections, a single-pole double-throw switch (S.P.D.T.) is used.

A double-pole double-throw switch (D.P.D.T.) is two S.P.D.T. switches in parallel. It can be used in the same way as a D.P.S.T. switch. By careful wiring this switch can be used to reverse the direction in which d.c. motors rotate.

When using mains voltages and in other situations when two wires need to be disconnected to completely separate an electrical supply from a circuit, a double-pole single-throw switch (D.P.S.T.) is used.

D.P.S.T. microswitch

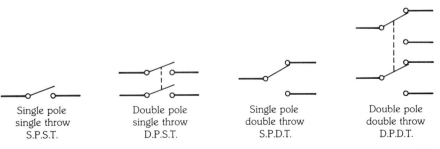

Single pole single throw S.P.S.T.   Double pole single throw D.P.S.T.   Single pole double throw S.P.D.T.   Double pole double throw D.P.D.T.

S.P.S.T.

S.P.D.T.

D.P.S.T.

D.P.D.T.

These photos show the connections at the back of four types of switch

Switches have to be used within their **current rating** or the contacts will burn out and the life of the switch will be reduced. Manufacturers supply data sheets that give a safe maximum rating for each switch. This is stated in terms of maximum safe current flowing at a particular voltage, e.g. 2 A at 240 V or a combined Voltage × Amps figure, e.g. 480 VA.

When a switch has to be operated by an electronic circuit, relays are used. A relay is made from a coil that becomes an electromagnet when a current is passed through it. This attracts a soft iron lever to the end of the coil. The lever's movement causes the switch contacts to be changed over. Relays are packaged to protect the fine coil wire and switch contacts. Any combination of switch contacts can be operated by the relay but the most common are single-pole double-throw and double-pole double-throw. More poles can be included. The coil is normally drawn as a labelled box on a circuit diagram. The switch contacts operated by the coil are labelled with the same reference number and will be placed elsewhere in the diagram.

Relay coil

Reed relay

Reed switches are operated by a magnetic field. When this field is produced by a coil the whole device needs to be protected. By encapsulating the coil and the switch in a package that matches circuit board matrix holes, a very small and neat package is produced. Reed relays can have single or double-pole switches.

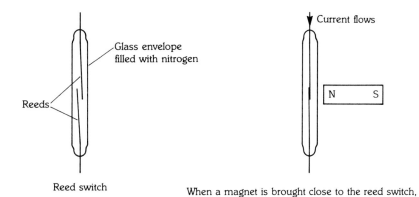

Glass envelope
filled with nitrogen

Reeds

Reed switch

Current flows

N   S

When a magnet is brought close to the reed switch, the reeds become temporarily magnetised. They attract each other and close the circuit. When the magnet is removed the switch opens again.

There are many types of switch:

Mercury switches	Rotary switches	Dual In Line (DIL) switches
Tilt switches	Micro switches	Rocker switches
Reed switches	Foot switches	Toggle switches
Contact switches	Slide switches	Miniature toggle switches
Knife switches	Key switches	Ultraminiature toggle switches

Transducers

There are a large number of transducers available for work in electronics. There are devices that will convert each of the following forms of energy into an electrical signal:

Sensing	Device		Symbol
Heat/cold	Thermistor		
Light/dark	LDR		

Sensing	Device		Symbol
Sound	Microphone		
Gas	Gas sensor		
Water	Water switch		
Pressure	Pressure pad/contact switches		
Movement	Switches, e.g. mercury switch/ Microswitch/Tilt switch, etc.		

Tilt switch

Sensing	Device		Symbol
Magnetism	Reed switch		
Rotary movement	Rotary switches		

These are all **input** transducers.

There are many **output** transducers that can be used:

Output	Device		Symbol
Heat	Heating element		
Light	LED, light bulbs		
Sound	Loudspeaker		
Bell	Buzzer		
Movement	Motors, solenoids		
Magnetism	Wire coil (solenoid)		

Transistors

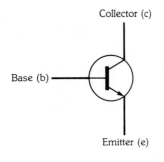

Collector (c)

Base (b)

Emitter (e)

Transistors are semiconductors made from a range of materials such as silicon or germanium.

The connections on a transistor are called the collector (c), base (b) and emitter (e).

There are two routes that electricity can flow through in a transistor. There is a path through the base connection to the emitter and a second path through the collector to the emitter.

How transistors work

It is easiest to explain how transistors work by using a simple example. In the diagram below the large horizontal pipe represents the collector–emitter connection. The smaller pipe connected vertically represents the base connection. Water can flow through the horizontal pipe when the sliding gate is lifted.

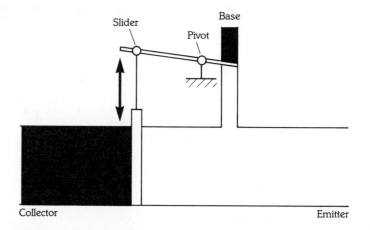

When a small amount of water flows down the thin pipe it causes the sliding gate to be lifted, opening the main channel and allowing water to flow from the collector side to the emitter side.

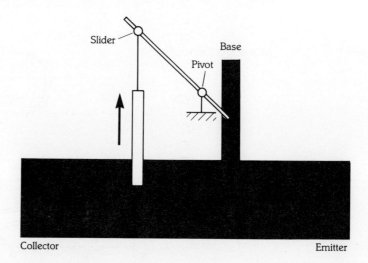

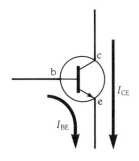

In a transistor the water is replaced by a flow of electricity. When the base connection is raised by about 0.6 V above the voltage of the emitter there is enough of a potential difference to cause a current to flow and fully turn the transistor on (fully saturate).

The symbol for the base-emitter current is I_{be}. The symbol for the collector-emitter current is I_{ce}. When a transistor is working a current is flowing through both of these routes.

As both of the currents flow through the emitter connection, the emitter current (I_E) is equal to the total of both currents.

$$I_E = I_{BE} + I_{CE}$$

The ratio between the base/emitter current and the collector/emitter current is the *gain* of the transistor and is represented by the letters h_{FE}.

$$\frac{I_{CE}}{I_{BE}} = h_{FE}$$

The gain of transistors is difficult to predict during manufacture. After completion transistors of the same type (e.g. BC108) are placed into groups a, b and c. Group a has the lowest gain and group c the highest.

If group a transistors are like Minis, then group c transistors are like Porsches. Both do the same job but one will be better than the other. A BC108c transistor has a better performance than a BC108a.

Transistors with the highest gain will perform well in every application. Transistors with a lower gain cannot replace a high gain transistor.

It is not possible to make transistors that have a high gain and a high current capability. The transistor selected for an application must be the result of a compromise, depending on what is required. There is a general trend of decreasing gain and increased current handling but there are some specialist transistors that have an exceptional performance and stand out.

Type	Gain	I_c max	Uses
BC169c	650	50 ma	High gain, low noise, audio amp
BC108	520	100 ma	General purpose
BFY51	123	1 A	General purpose
ZTX650	200	2 A	High speed power switching
2N3055	45	15 A	General purpose
BUR50S	55	100 A	High current, high speed power switching

Power transistors generate large quantities of heat as they conduct large currents. As a transistor heats up it conducts more electricity. This can lead to further heating and a situation called *thermal runaway* in which a transistor overheats itself to destruction. This can be avoided by using a metal heat sink which can absorb and radiate the excess heat.

Three designs of heat sink for power transistors

Index